MW00604904

Study Guide to Accompany

STATISTICS
A COMPUTER INTEGRATED APPROACH

Alan H. Kvanli
North Texas State University

Prepared by
John Brevit
Western Kentucky University

West Publishing Company
St. Paul   New York   Los Angeles   San Francisco

COPYRIGHT © 1988 by   WEST PUBLISHING CO.
50 W. Kellogg Boulevard
P.O. Box 64526
St. Paul, MN 55164-1003

ISBN 0-314-65692-8

CONTENTS

1

A FIRST LOOK
AT STATISTICS

Welcome to the fascinating world of statistical analysis! In the succeeding pages, we'll introduce areas of probability and statistics that have fascinated mankind for centuries, and techniques that have proven themselves useful in diverse areas of study from concerns for welfare worldwide to routine business procedures.

Some of these area--such as probability, statistical inference and regressions--occupy some for a lifetime. And there are areas of statistics we'll only allude to, to whet your appetite--and other areas we won't even mention, that could become your life's fascination!

The purpose of this STUDY GUIDE is to give you only a preliminary, perfunctory overview of each area-to make you a 'journeyman' able to handle statistical tools. To become a 'master,' you then need to study the text assiduously--and then work like a fool, to understand and appreciate the applications demonstrated in the examples and text problems.

We'll carry a few homey examples throughout this Study Guide -- a good deal to do with test scores in classroom situations, because it's familiar as well as illustrative. Your job is to project: the situation changes, but the analysis remains the same, or remains at least similar (in what ways?), or becomes entirely diverse (in what ways?) and so requires other methods of analysis.

The mathematics of Statistics, unlike that of some other areas of study, is never Cookbook mathematics. Every situation needs intelligent perception. Keep awake! Stay with it! You'll soon get a sense of the power of Statistics, and learn to enjoy it!

DESCRIPTIVE GRAPHS

Data will ordinarily come to you in seemingly indigestible form. The data below are a set of 100 randomly selected numbers. Such numbers can be generated, as they were here, from a table of random numbers or through use of a calculator or computer.

TABLE 1

100 Random Numbers

1.5	5.8	3.3	7.0	9.2
5.5	2.4	8.7	3.9	2.4
2.5	5.5	9.4	0.7	7.4
6.2	7.6	6.9	7.0	4.0
1.8	8.8	0.9	6.5	9.3
1.0	4.8	3.9	9.8	5.4
6.4	8.0	3.3	2.0	3.5
5.4	9.0	1.6	3.1	7.5
3.6	5.6	3.5	9.3	1.3
3.3	4.1	0.4	6.9	0.6
8.2	7.9	4.1	1.9	4.1
8.2	2.7	5.5	6.3	7.0
2.6	5.8	7.4	7.9	0.0
7.5	9.8	3.1	3.9	5.9
1.0	3.5	3.7	9.1	6.6
1.8	7.9	5.9	1.1	9.8
2.4	0.9	2.5	6.6	3.0
3.3	8.8	4.3	5.9	5.4
6.3	4.8	7.4	2.4	2.6
3.7	5.6	3.6	6.5	4.9

To create a histogram representing the data, you'll probably want to retabulate. You may observe that all data values are, in

this case, between 0 and 10:   a high of 9.8 and a low of 0.0.
Initially, you may decide on a display of five classes.   The
suggested formula: (H - L)/K yields (9.8 - 0.0)/5 = 1.96 and
suggests a class width of 2.00.   Tabulating the data into classes
might look like this:

Table 2

0.00-1.99	2.00-3.99	4.00-5.99	6.00-7.99	8.00-9.99
1.5	2.5	5.5	6.2	8.2
1.8	3.6	5.4	6.4	8.2
1.0	3.3	5.8	7.5	8.8
1.0	2.6	5.5	6.3	8.0
1.8	2.4	4.8	7.6	9.0
0.9	3.3	5.6	7.9	9.8
0.9	3.7	4.1	7.9	8.8
1.6	2.4	5.8	6.9	8.7
0.4	2.7	4.8	7.4	9.4
0.7	3.5	5.6	7.4	9.8
1.9	3.3	4.1	7.0	9.3
1.1	3.9	5.5	7.0	9.1
1.3	3.3	5.9	6.5	9.2
0.6	3.5	4.3	6.9	9.3
0.0	3.1	5.9	6.3	9.8
	3.7	4.0	6.6	
	2.5	5.4	6.5	
	3.6	4.1	7.4	
	3.9	5.9	7.5	
	2.0	5.4	7.0	
	3.1	4.9	6.6	
	3.9		7.9	
	2.4			
	2.4			
	3.0			
	3.5			
	2.6			

Contrary to expectation, perhaps, the number of values in each
class are not equal.   (After all, if the values are random, you
might expect twenty values in each class.)   This suggests, further
that we consider relative frequency as in

Table 3

Class midpoints	1.0	3.0	5.0	7.0	9.0
Relative frequency	.15	.27	.21	.22	.15

Now, consider a histogram to illustrate the distribution.

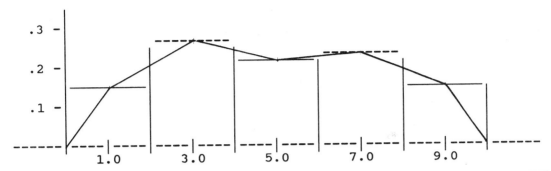

Since the data are considered to be continuous, the 'boxes' are adjoining. (A frequency polygon is superimposed to help the reader note trends.) Note that each box is centered at the class midpoint and coextensive with the class width.

While it is not very illuminating for this data, a cumulative frequency curve or ogive is illustrated:

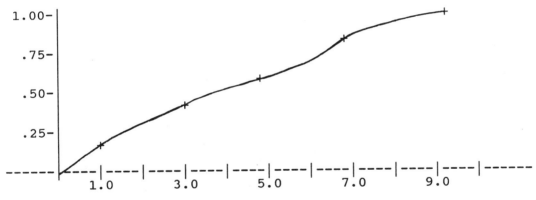

The desire here is to show growth: sporadic growth, or perhaps in another case, rapid initial growth followed by a slowdown.

Now that you've completed your analysis, you may step back, give yourself a pat on the back--or chuck the whole thing and start over.

Suppose you decide that your analysis is not 'fine' enough-- that perhaps more classes are called for, and you decide that ten classes are to be utilized. Here the class size formula becomes (H - L)/K = (9.8 - 0.0)/10 = .98 and suggests a class width of 1.

Since we have Table 2 at hand, it's no problem to create the tabulation below:

Table 4

0	1	2	3	4	5	6	7	8	9
0.9	1.5	2.5	3.6	4.8	5.5	6.2	7.5	8.2	9.0
0.9	1.8	2.6	3.3	4.1	5.4	6.4	7.7	8.2	9.8
0.4	1.0	2.4	3.3	4.8	5.8	6.3	7.9	8.8	9.4
0.7	1.0	2.4	3.7	4.1	5.8	6.9	7.9	8.0	9.8
0.6	1.8	2.7	3.5	4.3	5.6	6.5	7.4	8.8	9.3
0.0	1.6	2.5	3.3	4.0	5.8	6.9	7.4	8.7	9.1
	1.9	2.0	3.9	4.1	5.6	6.3	7.0		9.2
	1.1	2.4	3.3	4.9	5.5	6.6	7.0		9.3
	1.3	2.4	3.5		5.9	6.5	7.9		9.8
		2.6	3.1		5.9	6.6	7.4		
			3.7		5.4		7.5		
			3.6		5.9		7.0		
			3.9		5.4				
			3.1						
			3.9						
			3.5						
			3.0						

and also, in a similar manner, create a corresponding histogram
and frequency polygon:

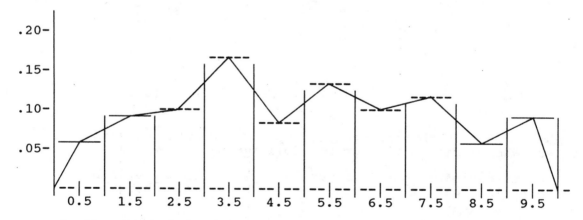

    Finally, your judgment comes into play: in which way will you
present the data? which is most useful? most illuminating? does the
increase in complexity (here, going from five classes to ten) aid
or hinder? Consideration of your audience is important.

The second tabulation yields more detailed information: will your audience appreciate having the gory details or will they become impatient? is the presentation oral or written? how much time will be spent in its consideration? You can mull over these and other matters that enter into your presentation.

Consider the Education table below, taken from Statistical Abstracts of the United States, 1981, prepared by the Bureau of the Census. No. 270. INSTITUTIONS OF HIGHER EDUCATION—NUMBER AND ENROLLMENT OF TOTAL AND OF FIRST-TIME STUDENTS, BY STATES AND OTHER AREAS: 1970 AND 1980

[Number of institutions for academic year beginning 1980. Opening fall enrollment of resident and extension students attending full-time or part time. Excludes students taking courses at home for credit, by mail, radio, or TV, and students in branches of U.S. institutions operated in foreign countries. See Appendix III]

STATE OR OTHER AREA	1970			1980								
	Total enrollment (1,000)	First-time students (1,000)	Number of institutions [1]	ENROLLMENT (1,000)								
				Total	Male	Female	Public	Private	First-time	Full-time	Part-time
U.S.	8,580.9	2,063.4	3,231	12,114.9	5,864.1	6,230.8	9,478.6	2,636.4	2,601.0	7,102.2	5,012.7
N.E.	560.1	141.5	250	765.6	366.3	399.3	390.6	375.0	166.4	477.2	288.4
Maine	34.1	10.0	28	43.3	21.2	22.1	31.9	11.4	9.9	30.2	13.1
N.H.	29.4	7.6	25	46.8	23.6	23.2	24.1	22.7	12.1	35.2	11.6
Vt.	22.2	6.0	21	30.6	13.8	16.9	18.0	12.6	6.7	23.1	7.6
Mass	303.8	76.1	116	418.4	200.5	217.9	183.8	234.7	89.9	261.4	157.0
R.I.	45.9	10.7	13	66.9	32.4	34.5	35.1	31.8	12.8	41.6	25.3
Conn	124.7	31.1	47	159.6	74.9	64.8	97.8	61.8	35.0	85.8	73.8
M.A.	1,433.6	319.5	555	1,821.1	871.3	949.8	1,102.8	718.4	355.7	1,147.0	674.1
N.Y.	806.5	172.1	293	991.8	470.9	520.9	563.3	428.6	182.4	634.5	357.3
N.J.	216.1	56.9	62	321.6	148.1	173.5	247.0	74.6	64.7	168.5	153.1
Pa.	411.0	90.5	200	507.7	252.3	255.4	292.5	215.2	108.6	344.0	163.8
E.N.C.	1,615.9	388.7	524	2,169.9	1,059.0	1,110.9	1,751.6	418.3	516.1	1,270.3	899.5
Ohio	376.3	68.4	135	489.1	242.7	246.5	381.8	107.4	110.9	308.9	180.3
Ind	192.7	43.3	74	247.3	126.6	120.7	189.2	58.0	57.0	165.6	81.7
Ill	452.1	114.8	157	644.2	306.5	337.7	491.3	153.0	148.4	332.4	311.8
Mich	392.7	90.8	93	520.1	251.2	269.0	454.1	66.0	125.0	286.9	233.2
Wis	202.1	51.4	65	269.1	132.0	137.0	235.2	33.9	74.8	176.6	92.5
W.N.C.	685.1	165.8	335	878.1	436.5	441.6	680.2	197.9	205.2	593.3	284.8
Minn	160.8	38.7	70	210.3	101.5	108.8	166.0	44.3	43.0	143.9	66.4
Iowa	108.9	29.3	61	140.4	71.7	68.7	97.5	43.0	39.1	108.0	32.4
Mo	183.9	41.3	86	234.4	117.7	116.7	165.2	69.2	50.4	148.4	86.0
N. Dak	31.5	9.4	16	34.1	17.9	16.2	31.7	2.4	10.3	28.3	5.8
S. Dak	30.6	7.7	20	32.8	16.5	16.2	24.3	8.4	8.0	25.6	7.2
Nebr	66.9	15.3	30	89.5	45.3	44.2	73.5	16.0	24.4	55.6	33.9
Kans	102.5	26.1	52	136.6	65.9	70.7	122.0	14.6	30.0	83.5	53.1
S.A.	1,070.6	277.6	524	1,723.7	817.6	906.1	1,365.3	358.3	349.1	1,036.2	687.5
Del	25.3	8.8	10	32.9	14.6	18.3	28.3	4.6	8.5	21.8	11.1
Md	149.6	33.6	57	225.5	100.9	124.6	195.1	30.5	48.9	111.1	114.4
D.C.	77.2	10.4	18	86.7	43.5	43.2	13.9	72.8	14.6	49.2	37.5
Va	151.9	43.4	69	280.5	127.6	152.9	246.5	34.0	40.5	161.6	119.0
W. Va	63.2	15.9	28	82.0	38.5	43.4	71.2	10.7	16.1	49.5	32.4
N.C.	171.9	57.2	126	287.5	136.6	150.9	228.2	59.4	69.7	196.7	90.8
S.C.	69.5	23.8	61	132.5	66.3	66.2	107.7	24.8	35.4	94.5	38.0
Ga	126.5	27.6	76	184.2	91.0	93.1	140.2	44.0	34.9	126.7	57.5
Fla	235.5	56.9	79	411.9	198.5	213.4	334.3	77.5	80.4	225.1	186.8
E.S.C.	411.6	98.6	233	614.3	293.3	321.1	506.1	108.3	140.4	429.8	184.5
Ky	98.6	21.3	57	143.1	66.8	76.3	114.9	28.2	31.1	96.9	46.1
Tenn	135.1	29.1	77	204.6	99.0	105.6	156.8	47.7	45.0	137.6	67.0
Ala	103.9	25.5	57	164.3	80.1	84.2	143.7	20.6	40.6	119.5	44.8
Miss	74.0	22.9	42	102.4	47.4	55.0	90.7	11.7	23.6	75.8	26.6
W.S.C.	725.1	170.1	265	1,096.6	552.0	544.6	953.5	143.1	250.1	686.4	410.2
Ark	52.0	13.5	35	77.6	37.3	40.3	66.1	11.5	19.1	58.0	19.7
La	120.7	27.2	32	100.1	78.3	81.8	136.7	23.4	33.7	116.2	43.9
Okla	110.2	27.4	45	157.6	79.1	78.5	137.2	20.4	32.7	98.1	59.5
Tex	442.2	102.0	153	701.4	357.4	344.0	613.6	87.8	164.6	414.3	287.1
Mt.	452.8	107.9	146	657.7	330.6	327.1	581.4	76.3	150.2	380.1	277.6
Mont	30.1	7.3	16	35.2	17.6	17.5	31.2	4.0	7.8	26.2	9.0
Idaho	34.6	11.6	9	43.0	21.4	21.6	34.5	8.5	11.4	29.0	14.0
Wyo	15.2	4.8	9	21.1	9.9	11.3	21.1	(Z)	5.2	12.2	9.0
Colo	123.4	28.9	44	162.9	82.9	80.0	145.6	17.3	29.3	105.1	57.8
N. Mex	44.5	9.4	19	58.3	28.1	30.2	55.1	3.2	9.6	36.6	21.7
Ariz	109.6	25.9	28	202.7	98.0	103.6	194.0	8.7	61.3	90.2	112.5
Utah	81.7	16.6	14	94.0	52.4	41.6	59.6	34.4	19.9	67.3	26.7
Nev	13.7	3.4	7	40.5	19.4	21.1	40.3	.2	5.8	13.5	26.9
Pac	1,609.0	388.9	389	2,338.1	1,111.6	1,226.5	2,097.4	240.7	463.0	1,032.2	1,305.9
Wash	183.5	53.3	49	303.6	141.3	162.3	276.0	27.6	24.8	158.3	145.3
Oreg	122.2	37.7	45	157.5	78.3	79.1	140.1	17.4	45.0	91.2	66.3
Calif	1,257.2	284.8	268	1,806.6	859.8	946.7	1,617.4	191.2	373.4	747.8	1,060.7
Alaska	9.5	2.2	15	21.3	8.5	12.8	20.6	.7	10.8	5.7	15.6
Hawaii	36.6	10.9	12	47.2	23.6	23.6	43.3	3.9	9.1	29.1	18.0
U.S. military [2]	17.1	4.3	10	49.8	45.9	4.0	49.8	-	4.6	49.7	.1
Other [3]	67.3	16.2	38	137.7	56.3	81.5	60.7	77.1	37.5	106.9	30.9
P. Rico	63.1	15.5	34	131.2	53.7	77.5	54.1	77.1	36.3	104.1	27.1
Guam	2.7	.6	1	3.2	1.4	1.8	3.2	-	.7	1.6	1.6
Virgin Is	1.4	.2	1	2.1	.6	1.5	2.1	-	.2	.5	1.6

- Represents zero. Z Less than 50. [1] Branch campuses counted separately. [2] Military academies. [3] Includes American Samoa and Trust Territory, not shown separately.

   Suppose we concentrate your interest first on Total Enrollment
for 1980 (the fourth column of figures). The table overwhelms.
You decide to prepare a bar chart; since the table is conveniently
parcelled into regions, your chart will consist of nine bars--
certainly less mindwarping than fifty bars. So, assuming our
purpose is served, a bar chart might look like this:

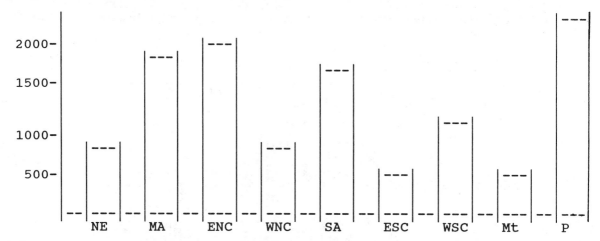

Can we answer questions, such as, where are the larger concentra-
tions of student population? where are the smaller? do these reflect population or run counter to population? (Now we would need
another bar chart--or a chart with double bars to each region: one
for population and a second for student concentration.)

   Perhaps we want to know the relative concentration of student
population east of and west of the Mississippi. If we combine
regions labelled NE, MA, ENC, SA, and ESC into EAST, and the remainder into WEST, we might decide to create a pie chart, as we
have here:

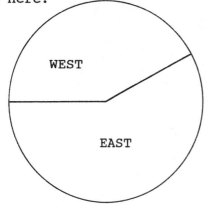

To compute circular area:

EAST: 7094.6   360 = 211.7
         12065.1

WEST: 4970.5   360 = 148.3
         12065.1

Perhaps of more current interest is the question: has student population, along with the general population, gravitated to the sun belt? Here, the census bureau's list of regions might have to be rearranged: is Kansas in the sunbelt and Minnesota not? let's assume so; is Wyoming not in the sun belt while New Mexico is? again, we'll assume so. How do we classify Colorado? Making such arbitrary decisions--and providing a map of the United States to aid our audience, we find student population divided thus:

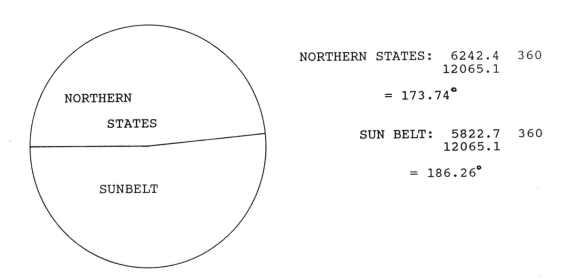

NORTHERN STATES: 6242.4   360
                   12065.1

     = 173.74°

SUN BELT: 5822.7   360
             12065.1

     = 186.26°

We've hardly scratched the surface of this single table. But keep in mind that charts, graphs, histograms, and the like, are pictures, and as pictures need focus. Too many facts crammed into a single picture can weary the observer.

PROBLEMS

1. Given a collection of random numbers (generated here off a calculator and rounded to tenths), prepare a frequency histogram of the data using a) five classes, b) ten classes.

5.3	7.3	4.2	3.8	5.5	4.5	3.8	2.8	6.9	3.7
3.7	6.5	3.9	2.7	2.3	8.0	4.5	6.9	8.1	0.2
1.2	6.5	0.7	5.7	5.7	3.7	5.0	6.4	7.2	3.0
8.8	6.0	6.9	6.1	3.6	8.4	2.5	7.4	9.4	3.9
3.5	3.1	2.0	8.9	9.8	8.0	6.7	1.1	2.5	9.8

2. Use the data of Problem #1 to prepare a relative frequency histogram, using five classes.

3. Construct a frequency polygon using the data of Problem #1 again using five classes.

4. Refer to the Education table once again. Prepare a bar chart comparing male and female enrollment in each of the regions specified by the Census Bureau for 1980.

5. Consider Table No. 272, again from the Bureau of the Census. In 1976, the last year for which figures are given, what percentage of total enrollment was Black, American Indian, Asian-American? Prepare a pie chart for total enrollment, showing enrollment for these groups along with those not included in these groups.

No. 272. ENROLLMENT IN INSTITUTIONS OF HIGHER EDUCATION, BY SPECIFIED MINORITY GROUPS, 1968 TO 1978, AND BY GEOGRAPHIC DIVISION, 1978

[Enrollment in thousands, except percent. As of fall. Prior to 1976, excludes Alaska and Hawaii. Covers full-time undergraduate students in 2-year and 4-year institutions taking credits equal to at least 75 percent of a normal load. Excludes federally controlled institutions. For composition of divisions, see fig. I, inside front cover]

YEAR AND GEOGRAPHIC DIVISION	Number of institutions	Total enroll-ment	BLACK ENROLLMENT		ENROLLMENT OF OTHER MINORITY GROUPS				
			Number	Percent	Total	Per-cent	American Indian	Asian American	Spanish-surnamed American
1968, total	2,054	4,820	287	6.0	169	3.5	29	48	91
1970, total	2,516	4,966	345	6.9	181	3.7	27	52	103
1972, total	2,665	5,531	459	8.3	219	4.0	32	57	130
1974, total	2,808	5,639	508	9.0	255	4.5	33	64	158
1976, total	2,821	5,755	605	10.5	331	5.8	38	101	191
1978, total	2,897	5,664	601	10.6	346	6.1	36	114	196
New England	236	395	15	3.9	10	2.7	1	4	5
Middle Atlantic	473	941	98	10.4	57	6.1	3	14	39
East North Central	467	1,016	99	9.7	24	2.4	4	8	13
West North Central	298	478	18	3.8	10	2.2	4	3	3
South Atlantic	494	832	158	19.0	24	2.8	3	6	15
East South Central	216	361	77	21.3	3	.8	1	1	1
West South Central	244	553	72	13.0	51	9.3	5	4	43
Mountain	129	306	7	2.2	29	9.6	6	4	20
Pacific	340	782	57	7.3	137	17.5	10	70	57

Source: U.S. Office for Civil Rights, *Undergraduate Enrollment by Ethnic Group in Federally Funded Institutions of Higher Education, Fall 1968* and, beginning 1970, *Racial and Ethnic Enrollment Data From Institutions of Higher Education*, biennial.

3

DESCRIPTIVE MEASURES

Some Elementary Analyses

        Once you have illustrated the data given to your satisfaction
--and to the satisfaction of your audience, even if you've gone so
far as to give vent to your artistic nature so as to make dry
figures more palatable, as illustrated here,

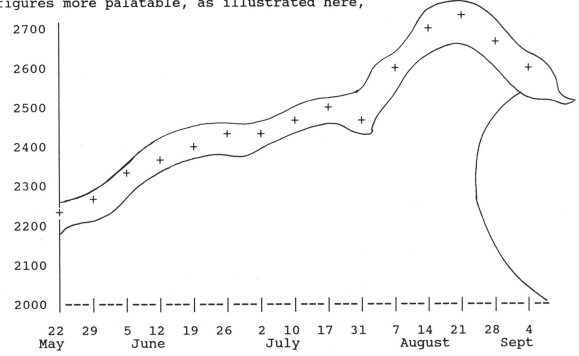

there remains a hunger for more information. If you are faced with a large collection of data--or even a smaller collection, questions arise: what is the average score? We'll find there are several scores we might call average, and lump them all under one heading as MEASURES OF CENTRAL TENDENCY. Another question: how widely do the scores spread? And again, we'll find several measures here under one heading as MEASURES OF DISPERSION. Still another: where does my score stand relative to the scores of others? You might have guessed that there is more than one way to judge. We'll lump these under the one heading as MEASURES OF POSITION.

A Simple Data Set

Consider the plight of an instructor of the Calculus. He gives a final examination to his group of Summer students with the following results:

35	23	20	11	25
48	16	9	15	34
31	50	10	25	25
36	6	20	26	23
15	16	10	32	16

To give the data some semblance of organization, let's do a quick and easy stem & leaf plot. The 'stem' below is the tens digit; the 'leaf' is the units digits:

```
0 | 6, 9
1 | 5, 6, 6, 0, 0, 1, 5, 6
2 | 3, 0, 0, 5, 6, 5, 5, 3
3 | 5, 1, 6, 2, 4
4 | 8
5 | 0
```

Notice, there's no attempt to order the digits in the leaf: take 'em as they come. But the result is at least in the spirit of the previous chapter: we may not pick or choose our class intervals with such care, but we do achieve a feel for the grade distribution

So, where do we go from here? How would our harried instructor assign letter grades, for instance? Surely, with a low of 6 and a high of 50, he wouldn't flunk the whole class! We're not even told what sort of scale was initially specified: was 100 a possible score? The instructor has long since departed with whatever scheme he may have had in mind. So, let's our bit for good ol' Watsamata U.

Measures of Central Tendency

    With the aid of a hand calculator, we can, for instance, find
the MEAN. If we consider the class as a 'sample,' with the 'population' all classes studying the calculus from the given text at
the Summer session (or, even more broadly, those studying the calculus from the given text with the given syllabus everywhere), we
can compute the mean for the sample:

$$\overline{x} = [x(1) + x(2) + \ldots + x(25)]/25 = 23.08$$

    How does the mean compare with other measures of central ten-
dency? The MEDIAN is the middle value; in our sample, the thirteenth score if the scores are lined up in increasing (or decreasing) order. We can glance at our stem & leaf plot and find our
median, Md = 23.

    Glancing may not always be most efficient. You may want to
note that there are two entries for stem 0, eight for stem 1, and
eight for stem 2. We want the thirteenth score: it must be in
the row for stem 2. Order the entries in the leaf:

$$2 \mid 0, 0, [3], 3, 5, 5, 5, 6$$

and locate the thirteenth entry, namely, 23. (Ten previous entries
under stems 0 and 1 and the third entry in the ordered array under
stem 2.)

    Alternatively, counting from the larger values, you'll find
two entries for stems 5 and 4, five entries for stem 3, and six
(for a total of thirteen) in stem 2 (counting from the right since
we've ordered stem 2 from smaller to larger).

    The median compares favorably with the mean as a measure of
central tendency. These measures don't always agree so nicely, as
we'll see.

    Another such measure, the MIDRANGE, is even easier to obtain:

$$Mr = [(\text{highest score}) + (\text{lowest score})]/2$$

For our data, Mr = [6 + 50]/2 = 23, an almost miraculous agreement
with the previous measures. On the principle of 'no pain, no gain'
these more easily obtained measures tend to be less useful. If a
data set contains 'outliers'--scores that are significantly higher
or lower than the rest--the midrange can give us a poor idea of
central tendency.

    Let's look at one last measure of central tendency, the MODE.
Here, we're asking: does some one measure occur with greater

frequency than any other? The answer for our data is no. We observe that two scores, 16 and 25 both occur three times--more occurrences than other scores, but not establishing a mode. Be warned about the mode: the mode--if it occurs--need not be near the middle. Too, certain scores--such as those on math exams-- tend to be, as indicated here, bimodal: a large collection of scores above the mean, and another pile of scores below, with a Bactrian-camel sag in the middle.

Measures of Dispersion

Before our enthusiasm wanes, let's also consider measures of dispersion. The first, and easiest, but unfortunately least infor- mative, is the RANGE, simply the highest score minus the lowest; for us: 50 - 6 = 44. As is true for other measures of dispersion, the range is a comparative score: are the grades for this class more widely dispersed (less so) than grades for other classes with which it might be logically compared?

Since we have the mean, let's find the MEAN ABSOLUTE DEVIATION with the marvelous acronym,

$$MAD = [SUM(i=1 \text{ to } n)|x(i) - \bar{x}|]/n$$

which for our data yields 216.24/25 or 8.65.

Correspondingly, the VARIANCE of our sample is given by the value

$$s^2 = SUM[x(i) - \bar{x}]^2/(n-1)$$

and the STANDARD DEVIATION by s. With the good offices of our calculator, these figures are 133.91 and 11.57, respectively.

Finally, in this area of dispersion measures, the COEFFICIENT OF VARIATION is given by

$$CV = (s/x)(100).$$

A relatively simple computation yields CV = 50.14.

We are still trying to help our instructor assign grades. Before we leave these measures, let's note one more thing: our mean, $\bar{x}$, was 23.08, and our standard deviation, s, was 11.57. Consider the grades that lie between one standard deviation below the mean and one standard deviation above the mean: the scores in the range, $(\bar{x}-s, \bar{x}+s)$, or between 12 and 34, inclusive. Note that 16 of the 25 grades lie in this range--64 per cent of the grades. Similarly, the grades within two standard deviations of the mean: $(\bar{x}-2s, \bar{x}+2s)$, or between 0 and 46, inclusive, include 23 of the 25 or 92 per cent of the grades.

If you are performing computations by pencil and paper, you might find computing the variance a bit tedious. There is a replacement for the formula, namely,

s^2 = [SUM(x(i) - x̄)^2]/(n-1) = [SUMx(i)^2-(SUMx(i))^2/n]/(n-1)

which is obtained by a bit of algebraic legerdemain. (Try it; it requires only a bit of observation to make the judicious substitutions.) The advantage is apparent for computation; using the grades from our calculus class, we construct the table:

x	f:frequency	x^2	x^2 f
6	1	36	36
9	1	81	81
10	2	100	200
11	1	121	121
15	2	225	450
16	3	256	768
20	2	400	800
23	2	529	1058
25	3	625	1875
26	1	676	676
31	1	961	961
32	1	1024	1024
34	1	1156	1156
35	1	1225	1225
36	1	1296	1296
48	1	2304	2304
50	1	2500	2500
---	-	-----	-----
577			16531

Now, SUM(x(i))^2 = 16531, [SUM(x(i)]^2/n = (577)^2/25 = 332929/25 = 13317.16 and finally

s^2 = (16531 - 13317.16)/24 = 133.91,

as before.

Measures of Position

A common student's question is, where do I stand relative to the rest of the class? Or, he wants to tell his parents, I'm in the top half of the class! To locate the pth PERCENTILE--that is, to establish the rank of a particular score or grade, we use the formula: n (p/100) where n is the total number of scores and p is

the percentile rank. For instance, which scores are in the top
half of the class? The formula tells us: 25 (50/100) = 12.5.
Rounding up (always), we are looking for the thirteenth score.
We just happen to have the scores in order in our table. The
thirteenth score is 23. Thus, scores of 23 or better are in the
top half of the class.

Again, which score is at the 90th percentile? By our formula,
25 (90/100) = 22.5. Rounding up, we are looking for the 23rd score
or, in this collection, 36.

Once again, which score is at the 80th percentile? Here, we
encounter a small problem: 25 (80/100) = 20 exactly. Rather than
take the 20th score (32, in our collection), we average the 20th
and 21st scores: (32 + 34)/2 = 33 for the 80th percentile score:
scores 33 and above are at or above the 80th percentile. In our
collection, there is no score of 33. But note that, with this
custom, 32, our first candidate, is below the 80th percentile.

Now, which score is at the third QUARTILE -- that is, which
scores are better than 75 per cent of the scores on the test?
Using our trusty formula, the 75th percentile score, or third
quartile score, is 25 (75/100) = 18.75. Rounding up, the 75th
percentile score is the 19th score, or in our collection, 31.

The second quartile score is the 50th percentile score, or
median, which we found to be 23. For the sake of completeness:
the first quartile score is figured by 25 (25/100) = 6.25 or the
seventh score, namely, 15. You might note that we have an annoying
duplication here: the sixth score is also 15. Playing the percentile game with just 25 scores is not strictly fair. The game is
usually played with thousands of scores on national exams, such
as the GRE--the Graduate Record Exam, or the LSAT, the examination
for entering law school candidates, and tests of similar magnitude.
Admissions officers will use percentile rankings (along with other
measures and other information) to accept or reject candidates for
graduate school, on the hope that such ranking will be an indication of prospects for success.

With the quartile scores at hand, we can sketch a box & whisker plot:

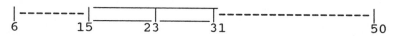

where we've extended our 'whiskers' to the extremeties of the data
and the 'box' shows the middle quartiles.

Earlier, while we were trying to assist our instructor to
assign grades, we noted scores ranging one and two standard

deviations around the mean.   The computations would look something
like this:

$$+/-1 = [x(i) - 23.08]/(11.57)$$

or $x(i) = 23.08+/-11.57$.   So then, scores wihin one standard deviation of the mean would lie between 23.08 - 11.57 and 23.08 + 11.57;
that is, between 11.51 and 34.65.   Since the grades given were
integer values, we enumerate the grades from 12 through 34.   In
similar fashion, finding the grades within two standard deviations
of the mean would ask:

$$+/-2 = [x(i) - 23.08]/(11.57)$$

and yield limits: -.06 and 46.22, and by the reasoning above include grades from 0 through 46.

More generally, we can obtain a Z SCORE by the formula

$$z = [x(i) - \bar{x}]/s$$

where the z counts the number of standard deviations above or below
the mean.   If grades are normally distributed (that is, if the
histogram, frequency polygon, or stem & leaf plot is bell-shaped
--or fairly close to bell shaped, then the EMPIRICAL RULE tells us
that about 68 per cent of the data should be within one standard
deviation of the mean and about 95 per cent of the data should be
within two.

The even more famous CHEBYSHEV'S INEQUALITY (if you're looking
up Chebyshev, check the spelling: you might find the listing under
Tchebycheff, or variations of these two; translators from the Cy-
rillic sometimes take liberties) tells us that, regardless of the
distribution (the distribution need not be normal or bell-shaped),
we will find at least 75 per cent of our data within two standard
deviations of the mean and at least 89 per cent within three.

Looking at the stem & leaf plot, we can see that the data is
not quite bell-shaped and our computations verify: instead of 68
per cent, just 64 per cent of the grades lie within one standard
deviation.   And, instead of 95 per cent, just 92 per cent lie
within two standard deviations. However, in statistics, close
counts. (We still have to define 'close.') We can make the
assumption that, given more data, the grades would tend toward
the normal distribution. (We could be wrong in our assumption:
we'd only know by testing a larger class or several classes under
near-equal conditions. No statistician would be happy with just
25 grades; he'd be most hesitant to make generalizations.)

The z-score can be used also to answer the question: how many standard deviations above the mean is the grade of 36? The computation would look like this: $z = (36 - 23.08)/11.57 = 12.92/11.57 = 1.12$.

If our instructor's practice is to assign the letter grade of A to any semester grade that is more than one standard deviation above the mean (unfortunately, every instructor has his/her own scheme; not all appreciate help from the resident erudite statistician), then all grades of 35 and above would receive an A.

Finally, we note that Chebyshev's Inequality is satisfied. At least 75 per cent of the scores are within two standard deviations of the mean (actually, 92 per cent are), and at least 89 per cent of the scores are within three standard deviations (actually, 100 per cent are).

PROBLEMS

1. Our instructor is assigned another Calculus class in the Fall. This time, the final grades look like this:

34	70
28	22
32	69
49	46
35	29
76	77
26	56
79	61
58	52

a) Construct a stem & leaf plot of the data; use the tens digit for the stem and the units digits for the leaf.

b) Find measures of central tendency: the mean, the median (with an even number of scores--18 grades here--the median will be the average of the 9th and 10th scores), the mid-range, the mode (if it exists).

c) Find measures of dispersion: the range, the mean absolute deviation, the variance, the standard deviation, and the coefficient of variation.

d) Find measures of position:

    i) the 50th percentile (2nd quartile) score. Compare with the median in (b).

    ii) the 1st and 3rd quartile scores.

    iii) Construct a box & whisker plot.

e) Find   i) the scores that lie within one standard deviation of the mean; what percentage of scores is this?

    ii) the scores that lie within two standard deviations of the mean; what percentage of scores is this?

    iii) what is the z-score of a grade of 70?

    iv) what is the z-score of a grade of 29?

f) Check that Chebyshev's Inequality is satisfied:

   i) Is at least 75 per cent of the data within two standard
      deviations of the mean?

   ii) Is at least 89 per cent of the data within three stan-
      dard deviations of the mean?

g) What percentage of the data lies within one- and two-standard
   deviations of the mean? Is the Empirical Rule satisfied?
   What does this mean for the data?

2. Freshmen at a state university are required to elect a course in
   mathematics. The course customarily chosen is General Mathematics. For one group of entering freshmen in General Mathematics, the ACT Scores were as follows:

23	26	12	17	10	15	12
14	15	16	14	11	21	24
13	15	16	21	10	19	16
11	9	17	7	6	5	21
16	9	8	14	21	24	6
17	13	10	3	13	5	18
14	18	14	12	12	8	17
11	1	14	14	17	17	19
16	8	19	9	6	15	4

We want the same information here as in #1. In part (e),
iii) and iv), find the z-scores for ACT Scores of 1, 3, 8, 9,
19, 21, 24, and 26.

3. The stock market graph on the opening page of Chapter 3 contains
   approximate weekly readings of the market's closing Dow Jones
   industrial averages. Presuming we have no other information,
   suppose we endeavor to enumerate the indicated prices:

May	22	2240
	29	2290
Jun	5	2320
	12	2370
	19	2420
	26	2430
Jul	2	2430
	10	2450
	17	2510
	24	2490
	31	2570
Aug	7	2590
	14	2690
	21	2700

```
        Aug 28                    2640
        Sep  4                    2560
```

Find the mean of these figures and the standard deviation.

HINT: Try encoding the data; subtract 2000 and divide by 10.
        Find the mean of the coded data and interpret.

WARNING: You don't want to gamble your portfolio--or any
          significant portion thereof on these approximations
          to the Dow-Jones closings!

PREVIEW: Means and deviations are of less interest than are
          trends; we'll look into these anon. But, be warned!
          trying to predict the stock market on the basis of
          past performance has seldom if ever kept anyone
          solvent.

4. Let's return for a moment to the Calculus class from last
   Summer. The grades ran from a low of 6 to a high of 50, you
   will recall. Just for the sake of argument, let's add one
   more student to the class. Our new student 'breaks the
   curve' by scoring 100 on the selfsame test. How does this
   new score affect our old measures? Find and compare: the
   mean, the median, the midrange, the mode. Which is (are)
   most (least) affected by the introduction of this 'outlier'
   among the scores?

   With the new score added, find and compare range, MAD, variance, standard deviation, and the coefficient of variation.

BIVARIATE DATA

Fortunately--or unfortunately--litle we do stands alone. The stock market nosedives in New York and Tokyo, and Gabby Jones loses his job in Milwaukee. The interest rate goes up one-half of one per cent and Molly and Johnny Smith have to pass up the mortgage they've hoped for. Before he becomes too lachrimose, effects can go the other way, too: Johnny (the very same) suddenly finds that the 1936 DeSoto he's been nursing along is declared a desirable antique and is now worth more than the house Molly and he had in mind.

More mundanely, let's return to the data we introduced in Chapter 3. Some students elect to take (or their advisors con- demn them to take) a General Mathematics class. We looked at their ACT Math Scores. Now, let's pair these with their scores on a 30-Question pretest given to judge their arithmetic skills. The pairs for each student (ACT SCORE, PRETEST SCORE) looks like this:

```
(23,20)  (26,26)  (12,10)  (17,24)  (10,22)  (15,25)  (12,18)
(14,20)  (22,21)  (16,21)  (14,23)  (11,23)  (21,22)  (24,28)
(13,19)  (15,20)  (16,23)  (21,24)  (10,11)  (19,27)  (16,23)
(11,21)  ( 9,30)  (17,29)  ( 7,26)  ( 6,19)  ( 5,21)  (21,30)
(16,26)  ( 9,17)  ( 8,17)  (14,23)  (21,20)  (24,27)  ( 6,22)
(17,27)  (13,18)  (10,21)  ( 3,16)  (13,24)  ( 5,12)  (18,24)
(14,28)  (18,25)  (14,22)  (12,18)  (12,18)  ( 8,12)  (17,25)
(11,21)  (14,19)  (14,15)  (17,24)  (17,21)  (19,27)  (16,25)
( 8,19)  (19,24)  ( 9,24)  ( 6,26)  (15,22)  ( 4,13)
```

What can we (should we) make of this mass of data? Will a student likely do as well on one test as on the other? (Both are math tests, but don't measure precisely the same subject matter.) We are asking whether the tests have a POSITIVE RELATIONSHIP, or in other words, are they so much repetition of the same matter that

we could do just as well with either the one or the other--and save
ourselves, and the students, the wear and tear of administering,
and taking, two tests when one would do?

Let's see what a SCATTER DIAGRAM might reveal.

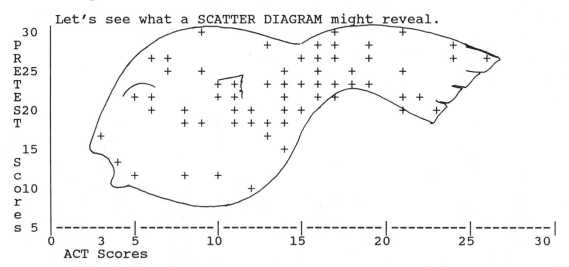

ACT Scores

We've examined our data: our highest & lowest ACT Scores are
26 & 3, respectively, and confined our graph accordingly; similarly
our highest & lowest PRETEST Scores are 30 (a perfect score) & 10,
respectively, and confined our graph accordingly. Such abbrevia-
tions of the graph might be desirable for legibility, but might be
undesirable if comparisons were to be made with graphs of other
data or if the graph thereby becomes misleading.

What have we learned? Is there a trend or are the scores for
all intents and purposes simply random? Could we predict that a
student who comes to us with a high ACT Score will score well on
the PRETEST? Well, yes, sort of. What about the converse? note
that a student with a score of 9 on the ACT (on a scale of 36)
scored a perfect 30 on the PRETEST(!) In spite of this truly ab-
berent score, we see something of a trend: students with low ACT
Scores TEND to score lower on the PRETEST; but not with the same
predictability as students with high ACT Scores TEND to score higher on the PRETEST.

Just for illustration, we've encircled our collection of
scores. A bit of reflection and we note that the scores at the
right--at the upper end of the scale--tend to 'bunch'; those on
the left--at the lower end of the scale--tend to 'scatter.'
Conclusion? How about: High-scoring people are more predictable.

But that's hardly mathematical. Can we put a number to our
observation? Fortunately, a number--called the CORRELATION COEF-
FICIENT, r, tells us something of the nature of the relationship
between two number sets. For our pairs, we want a number that
tells us: is an increase in ACT Score accompanied by an increase
in PRETEST Score--usually? then our Correlation Coefficient, r, is
positive; is an increase in ACT Score accompanied by a decrease in
PRETEST Score--usually? then our r is negative. (We'll ask a more
realistic question anon.)

The CORRELATION COEFFICIENT, r, is given by

$$r = SUM(x(i) - \bar{x})(y(i) - \bar{y})/SQRT[SUM(x(i) - \bar{x}) \; SUM(y(i) - \bar{y})]$$

$$= \frac{SUMx(i)y(i) - [SUMx(i)][SUMy(i)]/n}{SQRT\{[SUMx(i)^2 - (SUMx(i))^2/n][SUMy(i)^2 - (SUMy(i))^2/n]\}}$$

where the second line (messy as it looks) is easier for hand com-
putation. The correlation coefficient is designed so that $|r|<1$.

If r = 1 or r = -1, we have perfect correlation--and our
points in a scatter diagram such as that on the second page will
all lie along a straight line: if horizontal and vertical axes
are sketched as increasing left-to-right and bottom-to-top, respectively, in the usual way, these lines will slope UP for r=1
and slope DOWN for r=-1 reading the graph left to right.

If r=0, the diagram will be a random scattering of points with
no indication of a trend. In our collection, for the ACT-PRETEST
data r = .474. Well, again, what do we know? Our r isn't 1 (it
IS positive) and it isn't 0. Note page 116 of the text, Table 4.4,
for significant values of r--in particular, note that for n = 60,
in the table, r = .254 (our pairs number 62) which is to say that
values of r > .254 give us reason to believe that a correlation
exists.

Thus, for our ACT-PRETEST data, we are somewhat assured that
an increase in ACT Score will be accompanied, usually, by an increase in PRETEST Score. The value of r gives us a measure, an
indication, of the strength of that assurance: the closer to 1,
the greater that assurance.

How good of a predictor of PRETEST Score is the ACT Score?
Could we do without one or the other? Could we reshape either
one or the other to improve correlation? Do we want to? The
administrators of the tests would want to consider such questions
in light of the r-Statistic.

You might have noticed that we slid rather gracefully over
the computation of r: the formulas are rather forbidding and hand
computation lengthy. Fortunately, an inexpensive hand calculator
with statistic capabilities will do the onerous task for us.

PROBLEMS

1. One more glance at the General Mathematics data: how good of a
   predictor is the PRETEST Score for the FINAL GRADE in the
   course? Letting 4 = A, 3 = B, 2 = C, 1 = D, 0 = F, and -1=W,
   the pairs, (PRETEST, GRADE) look like this:

(23, 3)	(26, 4)	(12,-1)	(17, 4)	(10, 3)	(15, 3)	(12, 1)
(14, 2)	(22, 3)	(16, 2)	(14, 3)	(11, 2)	(21, 3)	(24,-1)
(13, 2)	(15, 3)	(16, 2)	(21, 3)	(10,-1)	(19, 3)	(16, 2)
(11, 1)	(9, 2)	(17, 4)	(7, 2)	(6, 2)	(5, 0)	(21, 4)
(16, 3)	(9,-1)	(8, 0)	(14, 0)	(21, 3)	(24, 4)	(6, 1)
(17, 2)	(13,-1)	(10, 2)	(3,-1)	(13, 1)	(5,-1)	(18, 2)
(14, 2)	(18, 0)	(14, 1)	(12, 0)	(12,-1)	(8,-1)	(17,-1)
(11, 2)	(14, 0)	(14,-1)	(17,-1)	(17, 1)	(19, 1)	(16, 2)
(8, 0)	(19, 2)	(9, 1)	(6, 1)	(15, 1)	(4,-1)	

   Follow the same procedure: draw a scatter diagram with pairs,
   PRETEST, FINAL LETTER GRADE); compute r. Draw any warranted
   conclusions.

2. Consider a correlation of a different sort. The mileage obtained by new cars driven at steady speeds for equal lengths
   of time on a cement track under nearly identical conditions
   for each trial are listed below:

MILES/HOUR	MILES/GAL
20	21.2
30	20.8
40	19.0
50	16.9
60	15.1
70	12.7

   Draw a scatter diagram with pairs (MILES/HOUR, MILES/GAL);
   find the correlation coefficient and interpret.

3. At a certain university, textbooks for a course are selected by
   a committee of instructors appointed by the department chair-
   man--usually four or more instructors who may have taught the
   course most recently. The committee collects and reviews the
   texts available and then ranks them. For example, two instructors on a recently appointed textbook committee ranked
   the texts under consideration thusly:

Text	Instructors I	II	d	d^2
1	8	5	3	9
2	2	4	-2	4
3	3	2	1	1
4	1	3	-2	4
5	6	8	-2	4
6	4	1	3	9
7	7	6	1	1
8	5	7	-2	4
				--
				36

Find Spearman's Rank Correlation,

$$r(s) = 1 - 6 \text{ SUM } d^2/n(n - 1).$$

Are the two instructors in essential agreement?

5

PROBABILITY CONCEPTS

We have need of some elementary ideas from the field of probability--and the language, both of which are essential to the study of statistics. To introduce these ideas, and this language, we'll be using a few simple examples: coins, dice, and cards. And we'll try to extend these ideas and language with the exercises into fields of greater interest. The examples from the field of gambling are used, not to assist you at the tables in Las Vegas and Atlantic City, (there's not much that can help you at the gambling tables; the rules favor the house) but because the examples are readily understandable and easily extended. Further, there's historical precedents: some of the initial essays into the field in the 17th century by Blaise Pascal and Pierre Fermat were in response to a gaming problem.

Probability values are assigned either A PRIORI or POSTERIORI --either before the game begins, or after on the basis of experimental data. Usually, when we make the assignments prior, we're doing so on the basis of an assumption: that the events under consideration are EQUALLY LIKELY.

Take a simple example. Toss a coin. The SAMPLE SPACE, the collection of possible outcomes, consists of HEAD or TAIL. If we assign probabilities A PRIORI it would only be reasonable to say that the probability of the coin landing HEAD up is one-half and that the probability of the coin landing TAIL up is also one-half. When would we NOT make this assignment? When we have some experimental data respecting this particular coin: if we've tossed it a sufficient number of times to know that the coin is not 'fair,' that, for example, it falls HEAD up twice as often as it falls TAIL up. (In which case, we would--for this coin--assign a probability of two-thirds for HEAD, and one-third for TAIL.)

Now, to assist us, let's use a bit of elementary notation:

29

let's assign H for HEADS, and T for TAILS, and write for 'the probability that the coin falls HEAD up' P(H) and for 'the probability
that the coin falls TAIL up' P(T), and make our assignments:

$$P(H) = 1/2 \qquad P(T) = 1/2$$

Notice a couple of things: all probabilities are between 0
and 1, $0<P(E)<1$, where we're using E to signify EVENT. Further,
the sum of the probabilities in any SAMPLE SPACE add to 1. If
$P(E) = 1$, we're saying that event E must occur; if $P(E) = 0$, we're
saying that event E cannot occur.

In our two-event sample space for the tossing of a coin, we
notice that each event is the COMPLEMENT of the other. The notation for the complement of H is H' (or H with a BAR over). We
could write, if we had the notion,

$$P(\widehat{T'}) = P(H) \text{ and } P(\overline{H'}) = P(T).$$

and we note that, for any event E, $P(E) + P(\widehat{E'}) = 1$.

Another Sample Space

Let's graduate to tossing dice: the first die can fall six
ways, and, since it's a fair die--or so we claim--each event is
equally likely; the second die, like the first, can fall six ways
with the same stipulations. Together, the dice can fall 6x6 or 36
ways: the sample space consists of pairs: (1,1), (1,2),...,(1,6),
(2,1),...,(6,6), where the first entry in each pair is the first
die, and the second entry is the second die, in a most natural
fashion. What is the probability, for example, that the first die
falls 2 up and the second die falls 5 up? or the pair (2,5) occurs?
Since there are 36 possibilities, each equally likely, the answer
is

$$P[(2,5)] = 1/36$$

There's another, more complicated way to look at this event.
(This is a useful complication, so bear with us.) We could name
event A: the first die falls 2 up, and event B: the second die
falls 5 up, and ask, what is the probability that events A and B
occur together? in other words, what is the JOINT PROBABILITY of
events A and B?

Event A occurs in a sample space consisting of six events:
$P(A) = 1/6$. In precisely the same way, $P(B) = 1/6$. So then, the
joint probability of events A and B, written P(A and B), can be
computed as

$$P(A \text{ and } B) = P(A) \, P(B) = (1/6)(1/6) = 1/36$$

precisely as before. But (there's always that 'but'), we've
glossed over an important consideration. This equation works only
when events A and B are INDEPENDENT. In fact, we'll take this equation as the definition of Independence (with an important codicil
to be added later). As so often happens with mathematical defini-
tions, this doesn't seem intuitive: suffice to say for now that
these dice don't know each other and don't influence one another;
each falls in its own 'independent' way without prior consultation.

Let's give our dice another toss, and ask what is the probability that either the first die falls 2 up OR the second die falls
5 up? We're using OR here inclusively: that is, we're saying
either the first die falls 2 up or the second falls 5 up OR BOTH
of these events happen. Since the sample space is relatively small
we can simply list the favorable events:

$$(2,1), \quad (2,2), \quad (2,3), \quad (2,4), \quad (2,5), \quad (2,6)$$
$$(1,5), \quad (2,5), \quad (3,5), \quad (4,5), \quad (5,5), \quad (6,5)$$

and ask again: P(A or B) = ? It seems 'obvious' there are 12
events, so that P(A or B) = 12/36 = 1/3. But, the 'obvious' here
is deceiving. We look again, and note that event (2,5) appears
twice, once in the first line and again in the second. It appears
that we're going to have to arrange to count the occurrence of the
repeated event just the once it deserves by a sneaky device:

$$P(A \text{ or } B) = P(A) + P(B) - P(A \text{ and } B)$$

so that for our collection P(A or B) = 6/36 + 6/36 - 1/36 = 11/36.
Having counted (2,5) twice (once because it occurs in event A and
again in event B) we subtract it once (out of the intersection of
the two events).

You might find it helps to sketch a VENN DIAGRAM of the situation. The typical Venn Diagram
for two events consists of four
regions: A int B' (event A in-
tersect B complement), A int B,
A' int B, and A' int B'. When
we count event A we count events
in A int B' along with events in
A int B. When we count event B,
we count events in A int B (again)
and events in A' int B. The events
in A int B correspond with 'A and B'
of our formula.

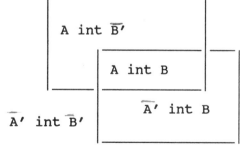

If this fascinates you, try
P(A or B or C) with the aid of a
diagram. (It gets complicated!)

Conditional Probability

Suppose we're given prior information about a probability? As you might suspect, the prior information affects the value of the probability under certain circumstances.

Suppose, for example, we toss a single die and ask, what is the probability this die falls 2 up? The obvious answer is 1/6, again assuming a fair die so that all possible events are equally likely. Now, suppose we have prior information: someone sneaks a peek and tells us that the die has fallen with an even number up. Since there are now only three possibilities (2, 4, or 6) instead of the previous six, the obvious answer is 1/3, under the same stipulations.

What has the prior information done for us? It has cut down our sample space: we no longer have to consider 1, 3, or 5 as possibilities. This CONDITIONAL PROBABILITY has a notation of its own. Let event A = the die falls 2 up, and event B = the die falls with an even number up. Then the probability of A given that B has occurred is written $P(A|B)$ and is computed as we've indicated, by restricting the sample space.

However, restricting the sample space is not always the simplest way to proceed. It may have cost us blood, sweat, and tears to figure the probabilities in the original sample space. Why go through all that again? There's a nice way to use the information from the original sample space:

$$P(A|B) = P(A \text{ and } B)/P(B)$$

In our simplistic example, in the original sample space, $P(A \text{ and } B)$ = 1/6 while $P(B)$ = 1/2. So, $P(A \text{ and } B)/P(B) = (1/6)/(1/2) = 1/3$, exactly as before.

Let's go back to our two dice example. If we are told that the first die falls 2 up, what is the probability the second die falls 5 up? We'll let C = the second die falls 5 up. We're asking for $P(C|A)$. By our formula, $P(C|A) = P(C \text{ and } A)/P(A) = (1/36)/(1/6) = 1/6$. But, all by itself, $P(C)$ = 1/6. The prior information seems to have been of no help whatever! Remember our 'under certain circumstances'? The circumstance is INDEPENDENCE. Since events C and A are independent (the dice don't consult one another), our $P(C|A) = P(C)$.

Putting a couple of things together: recall that we defined INDEPENDENCE with the formula

$$P(A \text{ and } B) = P(A)P(B)$$

Now, if events A and B are Independent, we know $P(A|B) = P(A)$, so we can write: $P(A \text{ and } B) = P(A|B)P(B)$. Further, since $P(A \text{ and } B)$ = $P(B \text{ and } A)$ (the conjunction 'and' is commutative), we can write, for independent events A and B,

$$P(A \text{ and } B) = P(B \text{ and } A) = P(A)P(B) = P(A|B)P(B) = P(A)P(B|A)$$

One more observation and addition to the language: consider our favorite die. Let's let event A = our die falls 2 up and event C = our die falls with an odd number up. What is the probability of events A and C occurring simultaneously? The obvious answer is zero: $P(A \text{ and } C) = 0$. Such events are called MUTUALLY EXCLUSIVE. Essentially, mutually exclusive events are events which cannot occur simultaneously. This, again, is a useful observation that can abbreviate computations. Consider, for instance, $P(A \text{ or } C)$. In general, we found $P(A \text{ or } C) = P(A) + P(C) - P(A \text{ and } C)$, but, for mutually exclusive events,

$$P(A \text{ or } C) = P(A) + P(C)$$

For our two events, A and C, $P(A \text{ or } C) = 1/6 + 3/6 = 4/6 = 2/3$.

Elementary Counting Procedures

To extend our observations in Probability to sample spaces of larger size, we're going to need some rules to assist us with our counting. We've been counting since first grade, but large numbers still can boggle the mind.

For example, if we flip a coin and toss a die, how many events are there in the sample space? We're looking at pairs: (H,1), (T,1), (H,2),...,(T,6). We can count these easily enough: there are twelve events. But we want to observe: the first experiment can result in two events, the second in six; they can occur in pairs in 2x6 = 12 ways. Which leads us to our first rule:

> RULE 1   If a first experiment can occur in n differ-
> ------   ent ways and a second can occur in m differ-
>   ent ways, then the two can occur together in
>   nxm different ways.

The rule is readily extended to three or more experiments. For example, if we flip a coin (2 possible outcomes), toss a die (6 possible outcomes) and choose a card from a standard deck of 52 bridge cards; if all possible triples [e.g., (H,4,Jack)] are equally likely, how many events are there in the sample space? what is the probability that is to be assigned to each event? There are 2x6x52 = 624 events and the probability assigned to each is 1/624. Listing all these events could take a while.

Now suppose we have several coins: a penny, nickel, dime, quarter, half dollar, and dollar (we must be back in Vegas), six coins in all. We have them lined up according to value right now. In how many ways might we line them up? Think of each coin in a slot: in how many ways might we fill the first slot? In six different ways with one of the six coins. In how many ways might we fill the second slot? In five different ways with one of the five remaining coins, and so on, until we're down to the last slot and the last coin. We can fill the six slots with the six coins in 6x5x4x3x2x1 ways, or 720 different ways.

This game of multiplying a counting number by all the numbers before it comes up so often that it has acquired its own notation: 6x5x4x3x2x1 = 6! In general, nx(n-1)x(n-2)x...x2x1 = n! with a special (useful) agreement that 0! = 1. The expression, n!, is read n FACTORIAL. The first few factorials are

$$
\begin{aligned}
0! &= 1 \\
1! &= 1 \\
2! &= 2 \\
3! &= 6 \\
4! &= 24 \\
5! &= 120 \\
6! &= 720 \\
7! &= 5040 \\
8! &= 40320 \\
9! &= 362880 \\
10! &= 3628800
\end{aligned}
$$

As you can observe, counting can quite quickly get out of hand. We need all the help we can get!

Let's take just four of our six coins--any four--and ask how many possible ways there are to line up four of the six. (All possible arrangements from penny-nickel-dime-quarter to dime-quarter-half dollar-dollar). Thinking again of each coin in a slot, we can fill a first slot in six ways, a second in five ways, a third in four ways, and finally a fourth in three ways: The total number of possible arrangements, then, is 6x5x4x3 = 360. Factorials come to view again--sort of. We could write: (6x5x4x3x2x1)/(2x1) = 6!/2! This may seem cumbersome, but scientific calculators do factorials nicely, so this is handier than might appear at first. In fact, there's a special name and notation: the arrangement of six objects in sets of four is called a PERMUTATION, and written

$$P(6,4) = 6!/(6-4)! = 6!/2! = 720/2 = 360$$

When we take all six coins and arranged them in a line, this too is a permutation: the arrangement of six objects in sets of six:

P(6,6) = 6!/(6-6)! = 6!/0! = 720/1 = 720

When we take n objects and arrange them in sets of k objects, in the manner we've described, we can write

Rule 2

P(n,k) = n!/(n-k)! = n(n-1)(n-2)...(n-k+1), n>k>0

A warning: be wary of formulas. They're of inestimable help where applicable; useless when not. Consider an example of a permutation of another sort: Mrs. Hospitable arranges a dinner party for six people. She is understandably concerned about who sits next to whom. Naturally, she will arrange her six people around the table according to her understanding of their compatibility. Let's leave her to her task and ask: how many arrangements are possible where the consideration is as it is here: who sits next to whom? The answer is not 720, the first number that might come to mind; instead the answer is 120 or 5! Think of it this way: seat everyone any one of the 120 ways; have everyone stand and move one seat to the right and sit down again. Everyone is in a different seat, but the 'arrangement' is identical. You could go through this charade six times for each of the 120 seating arrangements without changing the arrangement. This CIRCULAR permutation can't take the LINEAR formula.

Let's go back to our six coins. This time we'll ask the question: how many selections of four coins (each differing from the others by at least one coin) are possible? We've already done most of the work: we found P(6,4) = 360 where we were counting all possible arrangements of four coins from six. All we need do is to 'divide out' the arrangements and we're left with the selections: 360/4! = 360/24 = 15. The name for this is COMBINATIONS, and is written

C(6,4) = P(6,4)/4! = 6!/(6-4)!4! = 6!/2!4! = 15

Consider our hostess, Mrs. Hospitable, once again. She has twenty dear and close friends, but space admits inviting only four. If she were to choose among her friends in a random fashion (at this point Mrs. Hospitable is undoubtedly horrified; such a selection must never be random), how many selections of four are there? Does the formula apply? Yes, in this case, yes! We compute:

C(20,4) = 20!/(20-4)!4! = 20!/16!4! = 4845

which leads us naturally to

Rule 3

C(n,k) = P(n,k)/k! = n!/(n-k)!k! = n(n-1)...(n-k+1)/k!

Think of Mrs. Hospitable's problem thusly: since she loves them all, they must all love each other (no?); she decides to hold 4845 dinner parties. At a rate of 5 such per week, that's 969 weeks of dinner parties or almost 19 years of dinner parties. She might decide on a more judicious strategy.

Bayes' Rule

One last time (in this chapter), let's ask a question to which we have the answer: a die is tossed (a fair die, events equally likely); what is the probability that a five is tossed if we know that an odd number is tossed? Let's name the events: F = a five is tossed; O = an odd number is tossed. We want $P(F|O)$. Simply by limiting the sample space to the odd numbers: 1, 3, and 5, we see that $P(F|O) = 1/3$.

Now, let's use some of the machinery we've developed. We already know that

$$P(F|O) = P(F\ int\ O)/P(O)$$

and also that

$$P(F\ int\ O) = P(O\ int\ F) = P(O|F)P(F)$$

We might also consider $P(O)$ as

$$P(O) = P(O\ int\ F) + P(O\ int\ F')$$
$$= P(O|F)P(F) + P(O|F')P(F')$$

Putting these all together, we have

$$P(F|O) = P(O|F)P(F)/[P(O|F)P(F) + P(O|F')P(F')]$$

Performing the computations:

$$P(F|O) = 1(1/6)/[1(1/6) + (2/5)(5/6)] = (1/6)/(1/2) = 1/3$$

which we knew. But Bayes' Theorem is very powerful. Whenever we can divide a sample space into disjoint (non-overlapping) subspaces we can handle some interesting questions, as the problems will show.

Just one small extension: instead of partitioning the sample space into two disjoint subsets, we might want to partition it into three.

P[A(i)|B] = P[A(i)intB]/[P(A(1)intB)+P(A(2)intB)+P(A(3)intB)] =

P[B|A(i)]P[A(i)]/{P[B|A(1)]P[A(1)]+P[B|A(2)]P[A(2)]+P[B|A(3)]P[A(3}

where i equals 1, 2, or 3.

If you can stand one last simplistic example, let's ask: what is the probability a pair of dice falls (5,5) given the prior infor mation that the first die falls 5? We'll let A=the dice fall (5,5) and B=the first die falls 5 up. More than that, we'll PARTITION the sample space (the collection of all pairs) into three disjoint sets: I=all pairs in which the first member is less than the second II=all pairs of doubles, and III=all pairs in which the first is greater than the second. Let's list these sets:

```
 I:   (1,2) (1,3) (1,4) (1,5) (1,6) (2,3) (2,4) (2,5) (2,6)
      (3,4) (3,5) (3,6) (4,5) (4,6) (5,6)

 II:  (1,1) (2,2) (3,3) (4,4) (5,5) (6,6)

III:  (2,1) (3,1) (3,2) (4,1) (4,2) (4,3) (5,1) (5,2) (5,3)
      (5,4) (6,1) (6,2) (6,3) (6,4) (6,5)
```

In the notation of Bayes' Theorem, we're asking

P(A|B) = P(B|II)P(II)/[P(B|I)P(I)+P(B|II)P(II)+P(B|III)P(III)]

= (1/6)(6/36)/[(1/15)(15/36)+(1/6)(6/36)+(4/15)(15/36)]

= (1/36)/[(1/36) + (1/36) + (4/36)] = (1/36)/(6/36) = 1/6

To apply Bayes' Theorem, we've partitioned our space first into two and then into three disjoint sets. If circumstances called for it, there's no reason why we couldn't extend the number of partitions to any number required.

Problems

1. A class of students in General Mathematics attracts 45 students.
   While the class is normally populated by freshmen, a selection
   of sophomores, juniors, and seniors also elects the class. Of
   the 45, 30 are freshmen, 10 are sophomores, 3 juniors, and 2 are
   seniors. What is the probability that, in a random selection of
   one student,

           a) a freshman is chosen?

           b) a sophomore is chosen?

           c) the student chosen is not a freshman?

2. Of a group of entering university freshmen not all are coming
   straight from high school. A random survey shows the following:

	(A) Under 20	(B) 20 to 30	(C) Over 30	
(M) Male	26	21	16	63
(F) Female	22	6	9	37
	48	27	25	100

   What is the probability that a student selected at random will
   be
   a) under 20?
   b) female?
   c) male?
   d) male and under 20?
   e) either male or under 20?
   f) male if it known the student is over 30?
   g) Are events M and A independent?
   h) Are events M and A mutually exclusive?

3. The classification (Fr:freshman,...) and letter grade for a
   collection of General Mathematics students is as follows:

	Fr	So	Ju	Se	
A	7	1	1	2	11
B	13	3	1	0	17
C	13	4	0	0	17
D	10	1	1	3	15
F	11	0	0	1	12
W	22	6	4	1	33
	76	15	7	7	105

What is the probability that a randomly selected student is

  a) a freshman who passes with a C or better?
  b) an upperclassman (Ju or Se) who fails to either pass or complete the course?
  c) Are events So and Fr mutually exclusive?
  d) Are events So and Fr independent?

4. The registrar of a regional university finds that of entering freshmen, 73 per cent of the enrollment is from the immediate area while the remainder are from out-of-state. Of those who come from out-of-state, one-third complete their education at the university and earn the baccalaureate degree, while of the students from the immediate area, 48 per cent do so.

  a) Complete a contingency table, as we've done in problems 2 and 3. The columns might be C for Complete and C' for Incomplete; the rows might be I for students from the Immediate area and I' from those from out-of-state.

  b) Use the contingency table to find the probability that an entering freshman

      i) from the immediate area will complete his degree.
     ii) who does not complete his degree is from out-of-state.
    iii) who completes his degree is from the immediate area.
     iv) who is from out-of-state fails to complete his degree.

5. Consider two events with the following probabilities:

  P(A) = .40   P(B) = .70   P(A and B) = .25

  Find: a) P(A')
           b) P(A|B)
           c) P(A or B)
           d) P(B|A)
           e) Are events A and B mutually exclusive?
           f) Are events A and B independent?
           g) P[(A and B)']
           h) P(A' and B')
           i) P[(A or B)']
           j) P(A' or B')
           k) P(A|B')
           l) P(B|A')
           m) P(A'|B')

  Hint: For two events, or even three, a Venn diagram can save a great deal of time and make computations routine.

Try it! The difficulty is that for more events, the diagram becomes cumbersome--and we have to resort to other, more mathematical, devices!

6. Consider three events with probabilities

$$P(A) = .4 \qquad P(B) = .2 \qquad P(C) = .1$$

a) If events A, B, and C are MUTUALLY EXCLUSIVE [that is, if P(A) + P(B) + P(C) = P(A or B or C)], find

    i) P(A or B or C)
   ii) P[(A or B or C)']
  iii) P(A and C)
   iv) P(A' and C')

b) If events A, B, and C are mutually INDEPENDENT [that is, for all pairs, P(A and B) = P(A)P(B) and P(AandBandC) = P(A)P(B)P(C)], find

    i) P(A and B)
   ii) P(A and C)
  iii) P(B and C)
   iv) P(A and B and C)
    v) P(A and B and C')
   vi) P(A and B' and C)
  vii) P(A' and B and C)
 viii) P(A and B' and C')
   ix) P(A' and B and C')
    x) P(A' and B' and C)
   xi) P[(A and B and C)']
  xii) P(A' and B' and C')

Hint: Again, that Venn diagram saves miles of trouble!

7. There are five flights available out of Los Angeles to Chicago, another six from Chicago to New York, and seven from New York to London. Assuming all connections possible, the traveler has how many options from Los Angeles to London via Chicago and New York?

8. A university has three openings in the Statistics department and twelve applications on file. Assuming all applicants equally qualified, in how many ways might the three positions be filled from among the twelve applicants?

9. A committee of three is to be selected from among 12 qualified persons. How many different committees are possible? [We are assuming here that if the twelve are labelled A, B,...,L. a committee consisting of A,B,andC differs from a committee

formed ABD, etc.]

10. At an international conference, a round-table discussion among twelve heads of state is programmed.

   a) If the only concern in seating is who is seated next to whom, in how many ways might the delegates be seated?

   b) If two particular heads of state must NOT be seated next to one another, in how many ways might the delegates be seated? [Again, our only consideration is as in a)]

      Hint: Seat one of the recalcitrant heads, then the other (in how many ways?), then the rest.

   c) If a chairman and vice-chairman are to be seated opposite one another, in how many ways might the delegates be seated?

11. At our conference (problem 10), a committee of three heads of state is to be selected to monitor missile development.

   a) What is the probability the heads of state for the US, the USSR, and India are selected?

   b) What is the probability that, whoever else might be selected, the head of state of India is selected Chair?

12. The probability that you might catch the flu (F) this next winter is .42. The probability you might lose at least two days of work (W) if you do catch the flu is .74 whereas if you manage to survive the winter without the flu (F′), your probability of losing two days or more is .08. What is the probability you will lose two days or more work this winter?

13. A traveler overseas feels a bit nauseous and checks with a local doctor. The doctor declares forthwith that she is suffering from TB and must cancel the remainder of her trip and return home. The doctor fails to explain, however, that his test for TB is only 75 per cent reliable (that is, the probability the test is positive given she has TB is given as .75). The incidence of TB in the general population is about 1 per cent. What is the probability our weary traveler truly has TB? (That is, what is the probability of TB given that the test is positive?)

DISCRETE PROBABILIT
DISTRIBUTIONS

The random variable

A RANDOM VARIABLE, X, assigns a numerical value to each outcome of an experiment. We want to take advantage of some simple ninth grade algebra. Doing so might change our processes a little bit, but contribute a great deal to ease our work.

For example, when we flipped our first coin, we counted two possible outcomes: Head, to which we assigned a name, H, and Tail, to which we assigned a name, T. Then, assuming a fair coin-equally likely events-we assigned probabilities: $P(H) = 1/2$, $P(T) = 1/2$. With the use of random variable, X, we'll do something similar but not quite the same: We'll assign a NUMBER to outcome H, say 1, and a NUMBER to outcome T, say 0, and write

$$P(H) = P(X = 1) = 1/2 \text{ and } P(T) = P(X = 0) = 1/2$$

Again, when we toss our die, we might think in terms of a random variable, X, taking on values, $X = 1$ if the die falls 1 up, $X = 2$ if the die falls 2 up, and so on. The assignments don't have to match the dots on the die, but why be difficult? we make our assignments in the most natural way possible. In this sample space then, $P(X = 1) = 1/6$, $P(X = 2) = 1/6$, and so on.

You might have noticed in the title of this chapter that we're considering DISCRETE random variables, that is, random variables assigned to sample spaces whose events we can count. (There are two events in the sample space for flipping a coin; there are six events in the sample space for tossing a die.) We'll soon want to consider CONTINUOUS random variables--assigned to sample spaces taking on all values over an interval of values, where it might be impossible to 'count' all possible events, or simply inconvenient to do so. We'll consider, for example, the heights of all students

at a major university. Those heights might take on all possible
values from 4.5000 feet to 7.1666 feet. If we truly measure all
heights to 1/10,000 inches (with a laser?), we would, technically,
have 26,667 'events' to consider. That's just not statistically
viable; we're simply not going to assign probabilities to each of
these events. Instead, we assign probabilities to INTERVALS (for
example, to heights between 4.5000 and 4.7500). Here's where the
random variable, X, will become mandatory. This excursion into
discrete spaces will, if nothing more, give us insight.

Even in discrete spaces, the random variable gives us power.
Consider an example: let's flip two coins, and let random variable
X = the number of heads that might appear. Now, X can take on
values, X = 0, 1, or 2, with probabilities:

$$P(X = 0) = 1/4 \qquad P(X = 1) = 1/2 \qquad P(X = 2) = 1/4$$

Another example: let's toss two dice, and let random variable
X = the number of fives that appear. Again, X can take on values,
X = 0, 1, or 2, this time with probabilities:

$$P(X = 0) = 25/36 \qquad P(X = 1) = 10/36 \qquad P(X = 2) = 1/36$$

Once again, let's pick a card out of a standard bridge deck of
52 cards, and let random variable X = the number of kings picked.
This time, X can take on values, X = 0 or 1, with probabilities:

$$P(X = 0) = 48/52 = 12/13 \qquad P(X = 1) = 4/52 = 1/13$$

Up one step, let's pick two cards out of a deck of 52 cards
WITH REPLACEMENT and, again, let random variable X = the number of
kings picked. Now, X can take on values, X = 0, 1, or 2, with
probabilities:

$$P(X = 0) = .852 \qquad P(X = 1) = .142 \qquad P(X = 2) = .006$$

where the computation for P(X = 0) = (48/52)(48/52), for P(X = 1)
= 2(48/52)(4/52) [why the 2?], and for P(X = 2) = (4/52)(4/52).
You might notice that the probabilities add to .9999 rather than to
1 because of round-off error; we've rounded to fit!

Let's try the last WITHOUT REPLACEMENT. Either pick two cards
simultaneously, or pick one card, replace, pick another. Again,
let random variable X = the number of kings picked. Again, X takes
on values, X = 0, 1, or 2.

Let's compute the probabilities of this last two ways. First,
we write

$$P(X=0)=(48/52)(47/51) \quad P(X=1)=2(4/52)(48/51) \quad P(X=2)=(4/52)(3/51)$$

        = .8507   = .1448   = .0045

     Our thinking goes something like this: these events are not
independent--once we've removed the first card, the sample space is
reduced from one containing 52 elements to one containing 51. We
are choosing the second card from this new sample space; once we
acknowledge this reduction in size, the two sample spaces might be
treated as independent.

     To compute the probability for X = 0, for example, we observe
that the original space of 52 has 48 non-Kings, the reduced space
has 47 non-Kings. The thinking for X = 1 and X = 2 is similar.
One sticking point: the probability for X = 1 is multiplied by 2.
Why? The obvious answer is that it works! the probabilities now
add to 1. But that's hardly a reason. A moment's thought reveals
that we can do one of two things: choose a King first, and a non-
King second, or vice versa. We have to consider these as separate
events, much as we did when we flipped two coins and considered HT
and TH as separate events.

     A second way to compute these probabilities is the following:

          P(X = 0) = C(4,0)C(48,2)/C(52,2) = .8507
          P(X = 1) = C(4,1)C(48,1)/C(52,2) = .1448
          P(X = 2) = C(4,2)C(48,0)/C(52,2) = .0045

This time our thinking goes something like this: To compute X = 0,
the numerator says that we want to select none of the four Kings
and two of the remaining 48 non-Kings; the denominator says that
our sample space consists of pairs selected from the 52 cards in
the deck. The thinking for the other probabilities is similar.
You might note that there's no need to multiply by two to compute
the probability for X = 1. Why not? simply because the Combination
notation involves no order (you'll recall that we had to call up
Permuations to involve order).

PMF - the Probability Mass Function

     Our random variable, X, and the probabilities associated with
it, has a name, the PROBABILITY MASS FUNCTION. We've been writing
something of the sort: P(X = x), where the lower-case x has been
a numerical value and silently acknowledging that 0<P(x)<1 and the
SUM P(x) = 1, just as we originally stipulated for probabilities in
a sample space. As before, there's a gain that compensates for the
additional complication. Consider a simple example: we are given
a peculiar die to toss whose Probability Mass Function is

      P(X = 2n-1) = 1/4,   P(X = 2n) = 1/12,   for n = 1,2,3

which tells us that this strange die falls with an odd number up one-fourth of the time with an equal distribution among 1, 3, and 5 and falls with an even number up one-twelfth of the time with an equal distribution among 2, 4, and 6. As happens so often, the mathematical notation provides a sort of shorthand and lends insight.

On occasion, the PMF can be written as a neat formula (on occasion, it cannot; on occasion, the search for the neat formula can cost some head-scratching). Let's consider an even more peculiar die, whose PMF is given by

$$P(X = x) = x/21 \text{ for } x = 1, 2, \ldots, 6$$

We're to understand that once out of 21 tosses of the die, it will fall 1, twice 2, thrice 3, and so on. Do we truly have a PMF? We sum the probabilities to 1 and note that all lie between 0 and 1, inclusive.

Population parameters

Here, as before, we want to know Measures of Central Tendency and Measures of Dispersion: in particular, we want the Mean, the Variance, and the Standard Deviation. Our task is eased by the the assignments, either individually or by formula, to our PMF. In particular, the MEAN (symbolized by the Greek letter, MU) is given by

$$MU = SUMx(i)P[x(i)]$$

while the VARIANCE (symbolized by SIGMA SQUARE: SIGMA^2) is given

$$SIGMA \text{ SQUARE} = SUM(x - MU)^2P(x) = SUMx^2P(x) - MU^2$$

where the last equality is easier for hand computation.

For our last example, the PMF was $P(X = x) = x/21$, $x=1,\ldots,6$. The Mean, $MU = 1(1/21)+2(2/21)+\ldots+6(6/21) = 91/21 = 4.333$, and the Variance, SIGMA SQUARE $= 441/21 - 8281/441 = 21 - 18.777 = 2.222$. The STANDARD DEVIATION, then, is 1.4907.

We might compare this result with a standard, run-of-the-mill die with no peculiarities: the PMF now is $P(X = x) = 1/6$, $x = 1$, $\ldots$, 6, so that the Mean, $MU = (1+2+\ldots+6)(1/6) = 21/6 = 3.5$ and the Variance, SIGMA SQUARE $= 91/6 - 441/36 = 2.91667$ and the STANDARD DEVIATION, SIGMA, is 1.7078.

Observe that the peculiar die has a larger Mean (the larger values are more likely to occur) while the standard die has a larger Standard Deviation (the probability values are more evenly distributed; those of the peculiar die are 'bunched').

Particular Discrete Distributions

The UNIFORM DISTRIBUTION is the distribution we've seen more than once: when we flipped a coin with equally likely events, H and T; when we tossed a die, with equally likely events, 1,...,6, when we picked a card at random from a bridge deck of 52, we were paying homage to the Uniform Distribution.

For each event, x, in the sample space, $P(x) = 1/n$, where n counts the number of events in the space. You'll recall that for our coin, we assigned random variable X values 0 and 1 for Tail and Head, respectively:

$$P(H) = P(X = 1) = 1/2 \text{ and } P(T) = P(X = 0) = 1/2$$

--a particularly simple example of a Uniform Distribution. If we were to display the corresponding BAR GRAPH, each of the two bars would be of equal height: each of height to match relative frequency of .5.

Again, recall that for our die, we assigned random variable X values 1, 2,..., 6 and that $P(X = x) = 1/6$ for each assignment to x. Again, our BAR GRAPH would consist of six bars of equal height --each of height to match our relative frequency of .167.

For Uniform Distributions upon sequential counting numbers, the MEAN and VARIANCE are particularly easy to compute:

$$MU = (Min'm + Max'm)/2 \text{ and } VAR = (n \quad - 1)/12$$

For our die, then, MU = (1+6)/2 = 3.5 and VAR = (36-1)/12 = 2.9167. These are the same values we obtained earlier--with a bit more strain.

A second discrete distribution is the BINOMIAL DISTRIBUTION. If an experiment consists of a finite number of independent trials with precisely two possible outcomes to each, and if the probability remains constant from trial to trial, we have the makings for a Binomial Distribution.

Let's go back and flip our two coins again: we had a finite number of trials, 2; there were precisely two possible outcomes, Head or Tail; the probabilities remained constant, P(H)=1/2 and P(T)=1/2 for each trial. Let's re-compute the probabilities we had for the number of heads, X = 0, 1, or 2:

$$P(X = 0) = C(2,0)(1/2)^0(1/2)^2 = (1)(1)(1/4) = 1/4$$

$$P(X = 1) = C(2,1)(1/2)(1/2) = (2)(1/2)(1/2) = 1/2$$

$$P(X = 2) = C(2,2)(1/2)^2(1/2)^0 = (1)(1/4)(1) = 1/4$$

Let's go back and toss our dice once again. Just to make it more interesting, we'll toss three dice (will that do it?). What are the probabilities associated with X = the number of fives that appear? Obviously, X takes on values 0, 1, 2, or 3. We have a finite number of trials: three (we could think of this as tossing a single die three times); there are precisely two outcomes: either a five appears or it does not; the probabilities remain constant from trial to trial: p(5) = 1/6. We have a Binomial distribution, and

$$P(X = 0) = C(3,0)(1/6)^0(5/6)^3 = .5787$$

$$P(X = 1) = C(3,1)(1/6)^1(5/6)^2 = .3472$$

$$P(X = 2) = C(3,2)(1/6)^2(5/6)^1 = .0694$$

$$P(X = 3) = C(3,3)(1/6)^3(5/6)^0 = .0046$$

How do we interpret these probabilities? Well, for example, more often than not, you will see no fives on the dice; and, you probably won't want to bet on seeing three fives: in a thousand tosses, you may four or five--or not even one!

Here again, as with the Uniform Distribution, we find that the Mean and Variance are nicely accessible by formulas:

$$\text{Mean, MU} = \text{SUMxP(x)} = np$$

$$\text{Variance, VAR} = \text{SUMx}^2\text{P(x)} - \text{MU}^2 = np(1-p)$$

for the Binomial Distribution.

In our three-dice experiment, the Mean

$$MU = (0)(.5787) + (1)(.3472) + (2)(.0694) + (3)(.0046)$$

$$= .4998 \text{ (actually .5; we've lost a bit to round-off error)}$$

and the Variance

$$VAR = (0)(.5787) + (1)(.3472) + (4)(.0694) + (9)(.0046) - .2498$$

$$= .4164 \text{ (actually .4166)}$$

If we allow ourselves the use of the formulas, MU=np=(3)(1/6)=.5

and VAR(SIGMA SQUARE) = np(1-p) = (3)(1/6)(5/6) = 5/12 = .4166.

When the computations get messy, carry all the digits you
might need so that round-off error doesn't mislead you. As you can
see, though, the formulas for Binomial Distribution Mean and Variance take care of this problem nicely.

A third discrete probability distribution is one we've made
use of; it's called the HYPERGEOMETRIC DISTRIBUTION. We took advantage of it when we wanted to pick two Kings WITHOUT REPLACEMENT
from our deck. Once again, we need a finite population--as the
deck of 52 cards. We can generalize from this example: out of
k Kings, we want x Kings: C(k,x). Out of the remaining N-k cards
we want n-x cards: C(N-k,n-x). From the population of N cards
we want to choose n cards, altogether: C(N,n). Then,

$$P(x) = C(k,x)C(N-k,n-x)/C(N,n)$$

and, without further ado,

$$MU = nk/N \qquad VAR = k(N-k)n(N-n)/N^2(N-1)$$

In our example of choosing 2(n) Kings out of 4(k) possible
when the deck consists of 52(N) cards, MU = (2)(4)/52 = .1538 and
VAR = (4)(48)(2)(50)/(2704)(51) = .1392

If the ratio, n/N < .05, the Binomial Distribution can be used
to give an estimate of the Hypergeometric Distribution, using p=k/N
In particular, if we ask, somewhat as before, the probability of
choosing 0, 1, 2, 3, or 4 Kings out of our deck of 52, letting
p = 4/52 = 1/13, then we note the following:

	Hypergeometric	Binomial
P(X = 0)	.7187367	.7260
P(X = 1)	.2555508	.2420
P(X = 2)	.0249995	.03025
P(X = 3)	.0007092	.0017
P(X = 4)	.0000037	.00035

The two distributions evidently grow or wane together (their BAR
GRAPHS would look much the same) but are not identical. The Binomial misses rather grandly for the smaller values. (We wouldn't
expect them to be identical; else, why have two distributions when
one would do?) In pre-calculator days, when tables for Binomials
(for a few values of n) were utilized rather extensively, the estimate was an important way to avoid tedious computations.

We want to call attention to one last discrete distribution,
the POISSON, which is used to count the number of times an event

occurs in a specified interval of time (or some other measure: a distance, for example). As in previous distributions, conditions have to be satisfied: the occurrences have to be independent of the time interval (the number of soldiers kicked by a mule this month cannot influence the number kicked next month); the probability must remain constant from one interval to the next (traffic patterns counted between 3 a.m. and 4 a.m. don't compare well with traffic patterns at the same location between 5 p.m. and 6 p.m.); we want to avoid simultaneous occurrences: this is usually cared for by choosing smaller time intervals; we would like to think that the kicks or cars distribute themselves rather evenly over the interval we have in mind.

With all this in mind, our PMF for the POISSON is given by

$$P(x) = MU^xEXP(-MU)/x!, \ x = 0,1,2,3,...$$

Notice a couple of things: EXP(-MU) is the irrational e with exponent -MU. [The value of e is approximately 2.71828.] Further, the distribution is discrete (countable) but infinite. [If this sounds dangerous: how can the probabilities add to 1?, trust us for a bit.] We'd like to note, too, that the Greek letter LAMBDA is used in the place of MU in expressions for the Poisson, but the use of MU is significant: for the Poisson Distribution,

$$MEAN = VARIANCE = MU$$

Vera is a dealer at a Blackjack table (Vegas?) and notices (this girl is astute!) that during any thirty minute period there is an average of four winning hands that truly have Blackjack (by which we mean a Jack of Spades or Clubs together with an Ace). We find the probabilities that during a given thirty minute period she observes (i) no such hands, (ii) one such hand, (iii) two such hands, and so on. That is, we find

$$
\begin{aligned}
P(X = 0) &= 4^0EXP(-4)/0! = .0183 \\
P(X = 1) &= 4^1EXP(-4)/1! = .0733 \\
P(X = 2) &= 4^2EXP(-4)/2! = .1465 \\
P(X = 3) &= 4^3EXP(-4)/3! = .1954 \\
P(X = 4) &= 4^4EXP(-4)/4! = .1954 \\
P(X = 5) &= 4^5EXP(-4)/5! = .1563 \\
P(X = 6) &= 4^6EXP(-4)/6! = .1042
\end{aligned}
$$

and so on into the sunset for larger integers. The sum of the probabilities we show is .889326 (.8894 for the figures we show). So then, the remaining probabilities--for values of X greater than 6, must sum to .110674. Note too, that, while the Mean is 4, during any given thirty minute period, there are four blackjacks only one time in five (a bit less).

Finally, we can use the Poisson to approximate the Binomial distribution, just as we used the Binomial to approximate the Hyper geometric, with the stipulation that, in the Binomial, n is large while p is small. Again, finding these distributions comparable, under the right conditions, eases computations. With the advent of the scientific calculator, much of this has gone by the board, but the 'hierarchy' of approximations: the Poisson for the Binomial and the Binomial for the Hypergeometric, remains an interesting observation.

Problems

1. A quarter and half dollar are flipped. Let X equal 0 for a tail and 1 for a head on the quarter. Let Y equal 0 for a tail and 1 for a head on the half dollar. Form a contingency table for possible outcomes (x,y). Find probabilities for each outcome, assuming fair coins. Find the probability that the coins match, that is, that random variable X and random variable Y have the same values.

2. Random variable X takes on values 1, 2, 3, 4, and 5 with equal probability. Find P(X = 4). Find the probability that random variable X takes on an odd value.

3. Random variable X is defined by the PMF, P(X = x) = x/26 for for x = 2, 5, 8, and 11, and 0 otherwise. Do we have a legitimate PMF? Find P(X = 2 or 8). Find P(X = 5 or 11). Express each as a decimal to .0001.

4. An urn contains four white and six black marbles. Two marbles are to be taken at random from the urn with replacement. Our PMF details the number of white marbles taken: X = 0, 1, or 2. Find the probability distribution for X. $6/10 \cdot 6/10$ $4/10 \cdot 6/10 + 4/10 \cdot 6/10$

$4/10 \cdot 4/10$

5. Two marbles are to be taken at random from the urn in #4, but without replacement. For the same PMF, find the probability distribution for X.

6. Find mean and variance for the two PMF's in problems #4 and #5.

7. Random variable X takes on values 1, 2, 3, 4, and 5 with equal probability (see #2). Find the mean, variance, and standard deviation for X. Is the mean value what you might expect intuitively? What about the variance? could you have anticipated the value?

8. Random variable X takes on values 2, 5, 8, and 11, according to PMF, P(X = x) = X/26 (See #3). Find mean, variance, and standard deviation for this PMF.

9. A Binomial Distribution on five trials with probability of success 1/3 is given. Find the probability (i) the first three trials are successes and the last two failures; (ii) that in five trials there are three successes.

10. Random variable X represents the number of correct responses on a 10-question multiple choice exam with four choices to each question (one correct). If the questions are answered by guessing the answer to each, what is the probability of answering (i) six questions correctly? (ii) passing the exam--answering six or more questions correctly? Find the mean, variance, and standard deviation for this PMF.

11. Random variable X is binomially distributed with n = 12 and probability of success, p = .18. Find mean, variance, and standard deviation for this variable.

12. Twelve candidates for a basketball team suit up at the start of the season. If the choice is random, what is the probability the five starters from last season will start this year? Two junior college transfers are suited up for this season; what is the probability the two will start (given the same random choice)? What is the probability that either one or the other (or both) of the transfers will start?

13. A batch of chips shipped to a PC manufacturer is subjected to a random check. It is known that of 30 chips, five are defective. If ten chips are chosen, what is the probability that two will be found to be defective? what is the probability that at least one will be found to be defective? if this test is repeated under these conditions, what is the expected number of defectives found (the mean number) and the standard deviation?

14. We're just standing on the corner watching all the cars go by. In a half hour (by random survey; we've got more time than sense) an average of three Corvettes go by. If we stand on this corner this evening at five, what is the probability we will observe three Corvettes go by in the next half hour? is it possible that NO Corvettes might go by? what is the probability that we'll see at least one? that we'll see three or more?

15. Each year, in the pro draft, 240 athletes can justifiably be said to be 'eligible.' Of these, 12 are drafted by the Super bowl winner. If Hugo Hulk of Watsamata U. is eligible, what is the probability Hugo will be drafted by his dream team?

CONTINUOUS PROBABILITY DISTRIBUTIONS

The adjustment from DISCRETE Probability Distributions (Chapter 6) to CONTINUOUS Probability Distributions should not be a difficult one. As we did in Chapter 6, we'll consider some particular distributions: like the Discrete Uniform Distribution, we'll consider the CONTINUOUS Uniform Distribution, and, related to the Discrete Binomial, we'll consider the NORMAL Distribution, perhaps the most powerful of all. Finally, related to the Poisson of Chapter 6, we'll consider the EXPONENTIAL Distribution.

Given the data, how do we know which of the distributions we are to apply? one indicator is a HISTOGRAM. In Chapter 6 we knew we had a Uniform Distribution if the bar graph had columns of essentially equal height over each discrete value. The Histogram for the Continuous Uniform Distribution will be one (or more) rectangles over the intervals of domain values of the random variable.

Correspondingly, the Histogram for the Normal Distribution will be its famous 'bell shaped' curve, with essential symmetry dropping to left and right from its maximum height. Then, the Histogram for the Exponential will look like a ski-slope: one quick drop from left to right.

There will be other, more 'mathematical' indicators and we'll introduce some as they become essential.

The Continuous Uniform Random Variable

Consider an example: a bottling machine fills one-liter jugs. The machine delivers between .985 and 1.010 liters of cola to each jug. The distribution is uniform. What is the probability (i.e., for what percentage of the fillings) the machine will overfill? will deliver cola in excess of one liter?

Since the distribution is uniform and continuous (any value between .985 and 1.010 is possible) the histogram of the distribution is a rectangle on a base 1.010 - .985 or .025 long. How tall? Well, THE AREA HAS TO BE 1, to accomodate 100 per cent of the data. So, .025h = 1 and h = 40. To answer our question, we want to know how often the machine delivers more than 1 liter of cola, that is, in terms of the histogram, what is the area of that portion of the histogram resting on 1.010 - 1 = .010. The geometry tells us the answer: P(1 < X < 1.010) = (.010)(40) = .4 or 40 per cent of the time. Or, more algebraically (rather than geometrically),

P(1 < X < 1.010) = (1.010 - 1)/(1.010 - .985) = .010/.025 = .4

The mean amount of cola delivered and the standard deviation are given by

$$MU = (a + b)/2 \qquad SIGMA = (b - a)/SQRT(12)$$

where for us a = .985 and b = 1.010 -- the smallest and largest values bounding the rectangle of values for the Uniform Distribution. With our numbers,

$$MU = (.985 + 1.010)/2 = 1.995/2 = .9975$$

$$SIGMA = (1.010 - .985)/SQRT(12) = .025/3.464 = .0072$$

Decision time at the cola bottling works: we've collected our data, observed that our distribution is uniform, found an alarming bit of information - the bottles are overfilling 40 per cent of the time, been comforted by the mean - it seems well within acceptable range, and the standard deviation - the 'spread' seems reasonable. Do we allow the bottles to continue to overfill? That's what the management boys/girls do for a living.

A second example: Johnny's cruise control is set at 54 miles per hour for state route travel. As he lounges in his driver's seat--watching trucks, busses, and cars roar by at an average 70-- is he truly secure? Having nothing better to do, he watches the speedometer on the up-hill-down-dale state route vary uniformly (more or less) from 52 to 62 miles per hour. What is Johnny's mean speed? What is the probability (for what percentage of the time) his speed is in excess of the posted speed limit?

His mean speed is MU = (52 + 62)/2 = 114/2 = 57, and the portion of time he's in violation is P(55 < X < 62) = 7/(62 - 52) = 7/10 = .7 or 70 per cent of the time. Our boy had better sit up and watch his rear view mirror along with the rest of the speeders.

We may not meet the Uniform Distribution often on the road of life, but it is, nevertheless, useful in areas such as simulation.

The Normal Random Variable

We'll find, as we proceed, that the Normal is a most important distribution. We'll talk about sampling, and extracting statistics from our successive samples: the mean, for instance. Something wonderful happens: no matter what the original distribution--it might be a continuous Uniform Distribution--the collection of MEANS from successive sampling will turn out to be Normally distributed. No matter where you start, it seems, you ultimately find yourself at the Normal Distribution. It's like New York.

The area under the 'bell shaped' curve has to be 1 -- just as the area under the rectangle of the continuous Uniform Distribution was 1. But finding the area under the Normal is troublesome, so we'll holler for help: the text has a table of values, table A-4, and we're going to learn to use it.

For instance, suppose our shaded region (the figure at the upper left of the chart of Table A-4) were to give us the area under the curve from the mean (0) to one standard deviation above the mean: find 1.0 down the left-hand column, read the entry under the heading 0.00 for the row opposite 1.0. What do we read? The entry is .3413. We're to understand that 3413/10,000 of the area under the curve lies between the mean and one standard deviation above the mean.

Let's take advantage of the symmetry of the curve: how much of the area under the curve lies between one standard deviation below to one standard deviation above the mean? Just because of the symmetry, the area between one standard deviation BELOW and the mean is the same as the area between one standard deviation ABOVE and the mean. We found this last to be, from the table, .3413. Common sense says the area we want is twice that: .6826, or, as above, 6826/10,000 of the total area.

Once again, what portion of the area under the curve lies between the mean (0) and two standard deviations above the mean? As we did for one standard deviation, read down the left-hand column to 2.0 and find the entry under the heading 0.00. The entry is .4772. How much of the area under the curve lies between two standard deviations BELOW the mean and the mean? Exactly the same value .4772. How much of the area under the curve lies between two standard deviations BELOW and two standard deviations ABOVE the mean? nothing to it: .9544.

This might ring a memory bell: earlier we called attention to the EMPIRICAL RULE: 68 per cent of the values were to lie within one standard deviation of the mean and 95 per cent within two to satisfy the RULE. Now you know where the RULE came from.

Let's complicate things just a bit. We want to find the area under the curve between the mean and 1.25 standard deviations above the mean. Find 1.2 down the left-hand column, read across the row to the entry under 0.05. You should see .3944. We could write this as

$$P(0<z<1.25) = .3944$$

Now, find $P(.25<z<1.25)$. Since all table entries are values between the mean and a positive value of z, we'll have to find $P(0<z<1.25)$ - which we've done, and $P(0<z<.25)$ and subtract:

$$P(.25<z<1.25) = P(0<z<1.25) - P(0<z<.25) = .3944 - .0987 = .2957$$

Now, find $P(-.25<z<1.25)$. We have all the figures we need; use the symmetry of the curve: $P(-.25<z<0) = P(0<z<.25) = .0987$, and $P(0<z<1.25) = .3944$. This time we add:

$$P(-.25<z<1.25) = P(-.25<z<0) + P(0<z<1.25) = .0987 + .3944 = .4931$$

You'll find it truly an aid to sketch the 'bell' curve and shade the approprite region as an assist in using the table. Also, a WARNING: some tables of Standard Normal values give, instead of the area values from the mean to z, the area values from negative infinity to z. Check the graph at the top of the table when you're consulting a strange new table. The entry, for example, for z=1.0 will be .8413 (instead of .3413). To get the corresponding entry, simply subtract .5: .8413 - .5 = .3413. The argument is obvious: half the area lies below the mean: $P(NEG\ INF<z<0) = .5$ [just as half lies above: $P(0<z<POS\ INF) = .5$]

Back to the table: suppose we want to find the top 10 per cent of some scores--that portion of the area under the Normal curve that lies to the right, particularly so that the area is the last 10 per cent of the area to the right. A bit of common sense tells us, then, that 40 per cent of the area lies between the mean and the z value that marks our boundary. Obviously, we want

$$.1 = .5 - .4 = .5 - P(0<z<1.28)$$

where the table entry for z = 1.28 is .3997--as close to .4 as the table will let us be. We conclude that values of z larger than 1.28 will lie in the top 10 per cent of scores.

But what good does that do us? We've never seen scores of this sort. Test scores, for example, are on a scale of 100 with a mean, perhaps, of 70, not 0, and a standard deviation, perhaps, of 12, not 1. Fortunately, we don't have to have a new table for each new Normal Distribution; we can use Table A-4 for all Normal Distributions with minor adjustments. That's worth a prayer of thanksgiving.

Let's visit our General Mathematics group once again. We suspect that girls are more conscientious than boys, that even in this
required subject the girls tend to do better. Is our hunch justified? Let's look at the girls' final course scores:

85	98	61	55
86	82	48	60
97	94	82	64
82	78	96	54
93	82	50	57
95	73	88	70
91	70	61	59
80	80	71	76
35	74	65	67
82	73	77	61

as they were given to us from three classes. [These are the students who managed to complete the course. Several withdrew for var-
ious reasons. But that's another question: who have the greater
staying power, boys or girls? A data set can yield a great deal of
information.]

Using our hand calculator, we find the MEAN = 73.8 and the
STANDARD DEVIATION = 15.18. Let's ask the same question: which
scores are in the top 10 per cent of the class? Believe it or not,
we have the information we need: the score that marks the boundary
for the top 10 per cent of scores is

$$x = 73.8 + (1.28)(15.18)$$

$$= 93.23$$

If we were to order the scores:

35	61	76	85
48	64	77	86
50	65	78	88
54	67	80	91
55	70	80	93
57	70	82	94
59	71	82	95
60	73	82	96
61	73	82	97
61	74	82	98

we can easily see that scores above 93.23 are 94, 95, 96, 97, and
98, the top five scores.

While we have the scores ordered, let's ask another question:
are these scores approximately Normally distributed? They need not

be: math can be one of those frustrating subjects where some students learn the material readily and others struggle in vain. Let's
do a cursory check: is approximately 68 per cent of the scores
within one standard deviation of the mean? is approximately 95 per
cent of the scores within two standard deviations of the mean? The
scores within one standard deviation of the mean are:

$$(\overline{x}-s,\overline{x}+s) = (73.8-15.18,73.8+15.18) = (58.62,88.98)$$

or scores 59 through 88, inclusive. There are 27 scores (of 40)
in this range, or 67.5 per cent. The scores within two standard
deviations of the mean are:

$$(\overline{x}-2s,\overline{x}+2s) = [73.8-(2)(15.18),73.8+(2)(15.18)] = (43.44,104.16)$$

or scores 44 through 104, inclusive. Thirty-nine of our forty are
in this range, or 97.5 per cent.

Are the scores Normally distributed? Looks pretty good! 67.5
is mighty close to 68, and 97.5 is reasonably close to 95. Why
hesitate? Just as one Swallow does not a Summer make, one set of
scores does not a statistical conclusion make. We would prefer to
sample several times more under identical conditions before commit-
ing ourselves. Hastily drawn conclusions have embarrassed more
than one statistician.

We've avoided our initial question: do girls tend to do better than boys? we'll save that for the Problem Set.

We mentioned at the beginning of our discussion for Chapter 7
that the Normal (a continuous distribution) and the Binomial (discrete) are tied together. Consider an example: we make 12 tosses
of a die and ask what is the probability that three or more 5's
will appear? We'll let X = the number of 5's, and since the distribution is obviously Binomial (check that the conditions are satisfied), we'll write

$$P(X>3) = C(12,3)(1/6)^3(5/6)^9 + \ldots + C(12,12)(1/6)^{12}$$

or, to make the computations a bit more tolerable,

$$1 - P(X<3) = 1 - [C(12,0)(5/6)^{12}$$
$$+ C(12,1)(1/6)(5/6)^{11}$$
$$+ C(12,2)(1/6)^2(5/6)^{10}]$$

$$= 1 - [.112 + .269 + .296]$$

$$= .323$$

On the assumption that the Histogram for the Binomial and the Normal curve are comparable (this is truer for probabilities closer to one-half), let's see what the Normal gives us, after we've taken care of continuity:

$$P(X>2.5) = P[Z>(2.5-2)/SQRT(5/3)]$$
$$= P(Z>.5/1.291)$$
$$= P(Z>.3873)$$
$$= .5 - .1517 = .3483 \ (.1517 \text{ from Table A4})$$

where, since the distribution is Binomial, the MEAN = np = 12(1/6) = 2 and the STANDARD DEVIATION = SQRT[np(1-p)] = SQRT[12(1/6)(5/6)] = SQRT(5/3) = 1.291. Note the adjustment for continuity: since X=3 is included, we use 2.5 as our boundary value. (If we wanted values strictly greater than 3--4 through 12, inclusive--we would use 3.5 as our boundary value.) Our value .3483 (from the Normal) is an approximation to the Binomial value of .323. How close are we? Of course, if, as so often, accuracy is critical, we'd prefer the more tedious computation. But think of the possibilities: we have tossed our die just 12 times; suppose, instead, we had tossed our die 120 times (not out of the question!). The computations for the Binomial would need a Computer program, those for the Normal are not unreasonable.

The Exponential Random Variable

We found the Poisson Distribution useful for counting the number of occurrences--Corvettes passing a corner, for instance--of an event in a given time period. The EXPONENTIAL DISTRIBUTION is used to estimate the time between--when might we expect to see the next Corvette?

A Corvette just passed. We noted it in our tally. What is the probability that we'll see another in the next 10 minutes? Recall that we'd established that an average of 3 Corvettes passed each half hour. Ten minutes is one-third of our time interval, so we're asking P[X<(1/3)]. Now, the PMF for the Exponential is given by

$$P[X>X(0)] = exp[-AX(0)]$$

where A is the number of arrivals per half-hour (for our example). The MEAN = STANDARD DEVIATION = 1/A. For us, 1/A = 1/3 (A = 3).

So, to compute P[X<(1/3)], we'll find P[X>(1/3)] and subtract, that is,

$$P[X<X(0)] = 1 - P[X>X(0)]$$

For our Corvettes, P[0<X<(1/3)] = 1 - P[X>X(0)] = 1 - P[X>(1/3)] = 1 - exp[-(3)(1/3)] = 1 - exp[-1] = 1-.368 = .632, a reasonable

probability value, but then if three Corvettes go by, on the average, each half hour, seeing one go by each ten minutes shouldn't be
too surprising.

Not too surprising, either, the Mean = 1/A = 1/3 = the
Standard Deviation.

Since we're counting Corvettes, let's ask what is the probability that, having just noted a Corvette going by, we won't see another for a half hour or more? The computation looks like:

$$P(X>1) = \exp[-(3)(1)] = .0497$$

As the Corvette example indicates, the Exponential Random
Variable is essential to queueing theory. Banks, Supermarkets,
Restaurants, Bus Stops--wherever people have to wait for service,
have to give more than passing consideration to the Exponential:
just watch people impatiently switching queues at a Post Office.

One last note: we've written the PMF for the Exponential
Random Variable as $P[X>X(0)] = \exp[-AX(0)]$ where 1/A = the Mean.
Quite often, the Greek letter LAMBDA is used in place of our A.
There's nothing sacred about the custom; it does serve to tie the
two distributions together: the Exponential and the Poisson. Keep
it in mind as you check references.

Problems

1. Random variable X has a Uniform distribution with all value possible between -1.5 and 4.5. What is the height of the probability distribution? What is the probability that X is greater than 1.5? Find mean and standard deviation of the distribution.

2. Agnes observes that if she's just missed her bus, one will be along within the next ten minutes or won't show for thirty minutes and then might show anytime within the following ten minutes. If experience tells her that in either case, the distribution for bus arrival is uniform, what is the height of the distribution? What is the probability the bus will arrive between 35 and 40 minutes? Find mean and standard deviation of the distribution.

3. Find the following; assume a Normal random variable.
   (i) The probability, $P(-1.5 < Z < .5)$.
   (ii) The probability, $P(.56 < Z < 1.56)$
   (iii) The probability, $P(Z < 1.44)$
   (iv) The probability, $P(Z < -.47)$
   (v) Values of z such that $P(-z < Z < z) = .5$

4. Find the following; assume a Normal random variable.
   (i) Random variable X has Mean 70 and Standard Deviation 12. Find $P(52 < X < 76)$; find $P(76.72 < X < 88.72)$; find $P(X > 87.28)$; find $P(X < 64.36)$; find x such that $P(-x < X < x) = .5$
   (ii) Random variable X has Mean 70 and Standard Deviation 12. Find x such that $P(X > x) = .15$

5. For some classes in General Mathematics the final course grades for the males in the classes were

22	82	63	83	82
85	71	92	75	73
91	52	91	75	75
52	68	70	67	42
65	73	55	60	72
85	98	52	53	

Find the mean and standard deviation of these scores. Are the scores normally distributed (approximately)? that is, is some 68 per cent of the grades within one standard deviation of the mean? is some 95 per cent within two?

Compare the mean for the men with the mean for the women in

the same class (from our discussion). Which is the higher?
Is the difference between the two means significant?

6. Random variable X has a Binomial distribution with p, the probability of success, equal .4
   (i) If n = 10, find P(X > 8)
   (ii) Use the Normal to estimate P(X > 8)

7. Random variable X has a Binomial distribution with p, the probability of success, equal .4. If n = 120, use the Normal
   to estimate P(X > 96). [Note: this problem is essentially
   equivalent to #6, but the computations for the Binomial are
   prohibitive, and the answer is so simple!]

8. A local hospital has encountered its first case of Apehart's
   disease. If an average of six cases are reported annually
   throughout the country, what is the probability (i) the next
   case will not be reported for at least three months?
   (ii) the next case will be reported within the month?

9. The nozzle ring on a rocket is designed to last through an average of 48 minutes of burn time. If its life expectancy is
   an Exponential distribution, what is the probability the
   nozzle will be destroyed in less than the three minutes of a
   normal burn?

10. The average waiting time at the checkout counter of the super
    market is 16 minutes. Mrs. Gelt beats the game by putting
    her husband at the end of the line with an essentially empty
    cart while she shops. If she can normally complete her shop-
    ping in 18 minutes, what is the probability she'll catch Mr.
    Gelt before the clerk is ready to check him out?

STATISTICAL INFERENCE
AND SAMPLING

The Central Limit Theorem

When we sample from a population--whether we flip a coin and conceive that coin as representative of all coins (at least of all balanced coins), toss a die (the same conception), or use a group of students in a few classes of General Mathematics to draw conclusions that are presumed to be applicable to a much larger collection of students--we do so to obtain information. If the population parameters, such as MU or SIGMA are available--obtainable by reasonable means at a reasonable cost in a reasonable span of time --no one would bother with sampling. Sample statistics for the population mean(MU) and standard deviation(SIGMA) -- $\bar{x}$ and s -- give us information about the population at reasonable cost, in a reasonable span of time... You get the idea.

The CENTRAL LIMIT THEOREM (CLT) tells us that if we continue to sample from our population, if conditions remain as they are (or nearly so), we'll obtain a sample mean, $\bar{x}$, for each such sample and that the collection of means [one from each sample: $\bar{x}(1), \bar{x}(2), \ldots, \bar{x}(n)$] will be Normally Distributed with a mean, $MU(\bar{x})$ equal to the population mean, MU, or nearly so, and a standard deviation, $SIGMA(\bar{x})$ equal to the population standard deviation divided by the square root of the sample size: $SIGMA(\bar{x}) = SIGMA/SQRT(n)$. Intuitively, the means tend to collect at about where the population values are collected, but are less broadly scattered than the population values--and this scattering is influenced by the sample size: the larger the sample size, the larger SQRT(n) becomes, and the smaller $SIGMA(\bar{x})$ becomes.

Another way of saying this: the larger SQRT(n), the more dependable will be the value of the mean of the sample means: the smaller the STANDARD ERROR. Let's look at an example:

Once again, let's look at our students in General Mathematics. We'll list the 69 final semester grades for this helpful group:

```
85   95   82   80   92   50   65   68   59   67
22   91   94   74   75   52   75   70   65   61
86   80   78   82   73   88   77   54   73   85
97   35   82   85   48   91   55   57   76   98
82   82   73   73   91   61   60   70   55   52
82   63   83   61   82   75   64   67   60   53
93   98   70   71   96   71   52   42   72
```

Consider this group as our POPULATION. We'd previously found the mean and standard deviation:

$$MU = 72.116 \qquad SIGMA = 15.890$$

Now, let's play a little charade: our 'population' is too large and dispersed to find the mean and standard deviation. So we'll 'sample' our population to obtain a statistical $\bar{x}$ and s to estimate our population parameters, MU and SIGMA.

We'll want to do so legitimately--or as legitimately as possible. We'll form four sample sets, each of size 10 (too small! too small! say the statisticians among us) chosen randomly without overlapping (questionable from such a small population!) and see what sort of estimates we obtain. We'll use a random number generator, limit our choices to the numbers 1 through 69, and choose our samples sets accordingly. For each set, the first row is the number off the machine telling us which grade to pick, the second row is the corresponding grade:

```
I     #:   22,  18,  20,  15,  17,  11,   6,  27,  16,  24
      G:   80,  82,  83,  82,  78,  35,  82,  61,  94,  82

II    #:   21,   2,   7,  14,  45,  65,  50,  43,  62,  13
      G:   70,  22,  93,  98,  77,  61,  68,  65,  60,  63

III   #:    8,  59,  58,  40,  64,  29,  38,   4,  56,   1
      G:   95,  73,  65,  61,  67,  92,  88,  97,  42,  85

IV    #:   37,  25,  41,  48,  51,  30,  47,  10,  19,  54
      G:   52,  85,  75,  64,  70,  75,  60,  80,  73,  70
```

where we're saying that the 22nd grade is 80, the 18th grade is 82, and on down the list.

Now, let's obtain the sample means and standard deviations for each sample; from the rows marked with G:

	$\overline{x}$	s
I	75.9	16.475
II	67.7	20.742
III	76.5	17.865
IV	70.4	9.675

Consider the mean of these means: $MU(\overline{x}) = SUM\overline{x}/4 = 290.5/4 = 72.625$. Compare this with the true mean value from the population: $MU = 72.116$. Further, $SIGMA(\overline{x}) = 4.2797 = SIGMA/SQRT(10)$ which implies that our population value should be $SIGMA = 13.5336$. Compare this with the true standard deviation value from the population: $SIGMA = 15.890$. We seem to have done better with the mean (a fair approximation) than with the standard deviation (a seemingly poor approximation).

If the population parameters were unknown (as, usually, they are), how much confidence should we place in these sample values?

Confidence Intervals (CI) for the Mean of a Normal Population

Each time we sample from our population and find our sample mean, $\overline{x}$, we obtain a POINT ESTIMATE for the population mean, MU. As you can see from our petty example, not a single one of our sample means nailed the population mean. Even the mean of the means wasn't quite what we knew we wanted.

Let's ask a rather natural question: how confident are we that the mean of the first sample, $\overline{x}(1) = 75.9$, is contained in an interval which also contains the true mean? which, presumably, is unknown to us. Certain standard procedures are followed so that the results from one set of experiments might be compared with the results from another. For instance, it is not uncommon to ask for a '95% CI.' What does it mean? By this expression we mean (be careful with this one) that 95 out of 100 intervals formed as we will describe will contain the true mean. The other five will not.

Let's form our interval and see: we're saying that for a standard normal distribution, $z = (\overline{x} - MU)/[SIGMA/SQRT(n)]$, we want an area symmetrical about the mean that includes 95 per cent of the total area, leaving 5 per cent for the 'tails'--or 2.5 per cent in each. First question: what is the z-value that marks our area? From the table, we're looking for a z-value for a table entry of .4750 (half of .9500), or $z = 1.96$. We're saying that

$$P(-1.96 < z < 1.96) = .95$$

Transposing into the values of our illustrative example,

$$P(-1.96 < (\overline{x} - MU)/[SIGMA/SQRT(n)] < 1.96) = .95$$

or, with a little algebraic manipulation,

$$P(\overline{x} - 1.96[SIGMA/SQRT(n)] < MU < \overline{x} + 1.96[SIGMA/SQRT(n)]) = .95$$

Now, let's insert our values: $\overline{x}$ = 75.9, n = 10, and SIGMA is the standard deviation of our population, SIGMA = 15.890:

$$P(75.9 - 1.96[15.890/SQRT(10)] < MU < 75.9 + 1.96[15.890/SQRT(10)])$$

$$= P(75.9 - 9.8487 < MU < 75.9 + 9.8487)$$

$$= P(66.05 < MU < 85.75) = .95$$

Again, what are we asserting? That we're 95 per cent certain that the true population mean lies in this interval. We're saying that if we were to take 100 such samples, 95 of them would contain the mean, the other five would not.

With this petty example, the population mean, MU = 72.116, is known to us. (Under normal sampling circumstances, it would not.) And the population mean does indeed lie in this interval.

One nagging little point: how could we possibly know the population standard deviation, SIGMA, if we don't know the population mean, MU? We're proceeding on some assumptions: this population has been sampled time and time again. Our concentration is, presently, on checking the sample mean, utilizing whatever prior knowledge might be available. If this is our first essay into this set of values, we'd have little choice: we'd have to use the sample standard deviation as the only information available. Then, with SIGMA replaced by s = 16.475, our computations would look like:

$$P(75.9-2.262[16.475/[SQRT(10)]<MU<75.9+2.262[16.475/[SQRT(10)])$$

$$= P(75.9 - 11.785 < MU < 75.9 + 11.785)$$

$$= P(64.115 < MU < 87.685) = .95$$

where, in addition, we've switched tables. The values, 2.262 was obtained from Table A-5: under column t(.025), opposite row 9.

What have we gained or lost? This interval is wider (not by much), so we've lost a bit of certainty. In any case, the standard deviation from only a single sample would give us less confidence than the standard deviation from a host of previous samples, would it not? Yes, if, meanwhile, circumstances hadn't changed. You may have noticed that uncertainty is built in. That's why we're playing this game!

Do we want greater certainty that our interval contains the population mean? One way to increase certainty is to narrow the interval: ask not for 95 per cent certainty, but, perhaps, for 90 per cent certainty. The procedure is the same: we want the z-value that marks a symmetrical 90 per cent of the area under the Normal curve about the mean. We look for the z-value that marks an area off the table with entry .4500 (half of .90) and find that z falls half way between 1.64 and 1.65, and so set z = 1.645.

Everything else remains the same:

P(75.9-1.645[15.89/SQRT(10)] < MU < 75.9+1.645[15.89/SQRT(10)])

= P(75.9 - 8.2659 < MU < 75.9 + 8.2659)

= P(67.634 < MU < 84.166) = .90

Finally, we might want to proceed in just the opposite direction. Ask for 99 per cent certainty that the interval contains the population mean: broaden the interval. Find the z-value which marks a symmetrical 99 per cent of the area under the Normal curve about the mean. Again, to the table: we're looking for the z with entry .4950 (half of .99): z = 2.58 (z = 2.575 off our table, but z = 2.58 is closer--and custom dictates...).

Once again, at our sample:

P(75.9-2.58[15.89/SQRT(10)] < MU < 75.9+2.58[15.89/SQRT(10)])

= P(75.9 - 12.964 < MU < 75.9 + 12.964)

= P(62.936 < MU < 88.864) = .99

Our certainty is greater, but the interval may be so broad now as to be useless. In any case, it's up to the experimenter to decide--and to try to convince his auditors. Each of these CONFIDENCE INTERVALS are in common usage: 95% CI, 90% CI, or, the last, 99% CI.

You undoubtedly noticed that when we used the sample standard deviation we switched to Table A-5, the t-DISTRIBUTION. The net effect was to increase the multiplier (from 1.645 to 2.262) and to broaden the interval, and thus decreasing certainty. Particularly in circumstances such as ours: small sample size and sample statistics, the t-distribution is the more reliable.

The subscript on t measures the area under the curve to the

right of the mark, t(ALPHA). Since, for a 95% CI, the area to
the right of the mark is ALPHA = .025 (half of .05), we use the
values in this column. We chose degrees of freedom (df) equal to
9 to indicate that our sample size was 10 (df = 10-1 = 9; in each
case, df = n-1, where n is the sample size).

Let's review: we address a population, such as our General
Mathematics final scores, and, supposing the population parameter
we desire, the Mean, in this case, is inaccessible, take a sample,
and find a corresponding sample statistic, $\bar{x}$. Suppose, this time,
we take the results of the second sample, $\bar{x}$ = 67.7. Quite different from the mean of the first sample (75.9)! Again, how might we
express confidence in this sample statistic? We choose an interval
that expresses our confidence, say a 95% CI, and write

$$P(67.7-1.96[15.89/SQRT(10) < MU < 67.7-1.96[15.89/SQRT(10)])$$

$$= P(67.7 - 9.8487 < MU < 67.7 + 9.8487)$$

$$= P(57.85 < MU < 77.55) = .95$$

and ask: does this interval contain the true population mean? In
the absence of information, we say that were we to take 100 samples
such as these, 95 would contain the mean, the remaining five would
not. (This is the second; 98 more to go!)

If we didn't have access to the population standard deviation,
we would use our sample value: 20.742, and resort to the t-distribution for our multiplier, supposing that the original distribution
is Normal. One more look at Table A-5: the last meaningful value
is df = 30. For larger sample size, the t-distributions and the
standard normal are almost identical, and, even for problems such
as ours: sample statistic for the standard deviation value, we'd
utilize the standard normal table.

Sample size

You've heard survey results given, particularly for political
candidates favored by the electorate, with the qualification: 'plus
or minus three percentage points.' How do pollsters manage to control the ERROR so closely? In a sense, we've already done the job:
when we added and subtracted 1.96(SIGMA/SQRT(n), we were placing
bounds in response to our specification that we wanted a 95% CI or
no more than a 2.5 per cent error.

Now, specifying the error we agree we can live with, let's
find the size sample we need: we specify the pollster's favorite
'plus or minus three percentage points.' From the Standard Normal
table, we find the corresponding z-value: if 3 per cent of the
values are in the 'tail,' then 47 per cent lies to left, and z=1.88
(the table entry is .4699 rather than .47). Using our SIGMA from

the population, SIGMA = 15.89, we're saying:

$$ERROR = 3 = 1.88[15.89/SQRT(n)]$$

or, solving for SQRT(n),

$$SQRT(n) = (1.88)(15.89)/3 = 9.96 \text{ and } n = 99.2$$

Rounding up (always), we are told that, to obtain the desired accuracy, we need a sample size of n = 100.

Note that the Error is given in percentage points; this, in turn, specificies the Confidence Interval. The standard deviation is known, or is estimated by using sample standard deviation. But when you do use the sample statistic, keep in mind that the error encountered may be greater: the new standard deviation may differ, sometimes significantly, from the population standard deviation.

A quick and easy check on the standard deviation is given by noting that 2(.5-.4772) = 2(.0228) = .0456 or 4.56 per cent of all data for a Normal distribution lies outside two standard deviations from the mean. What remains: about 95 per cent, then, is retained within. It follows that if we take the Highest and Lowest scores, we'll find them spread across about four standard deviations. Thus, a rough estimate of the standard deviation is

$$SIGMA = (H - L)/4$$

Let's try it: Our first sample from the General Mathematics class data: 80, 82, 83, 82, 78, 35, 82, 61, 94, 82, had a mean of 75.9 and a standard deviation of 16.475, by laborious computation, (or use of a calculator). By our observation,

$$SIGMA = (94 - 35)/4 = 14.75$$

A bit narrow, but not totally out of range.

The second sample data: 70, 22, 93, 98, 77, 61, 68, 65, 60, 63, had a mean of 67.7 and standard deviation of 20.742. By our observation,

$$SIGMA = (98 - 22)/4 = 19.0$$

Again, a bit narrow, but responsive to the data.

For the two remaining samples, our formula: s = (H - L)/4, gives us values s = 13.75 (s = 17.865 by computation) for sample III, and s = 8.25 (s = 9.675 by computation) for sample IV. In each case, the sample standard deviation is somewhat larger than the value obtained by the formula, but not entirely out of line.

Problems

1. Suppose $\bar{x}$ is the sample mean from a normally distributed population with mean MU = 50 and standard deviation SIGMA = 10.
   The sample size, n = 12. Find the probabilities:
       (a) P(x > 56)
       (b) P(x > 44)
       (c) P(44 < x < 56)
       (d) P(x < 44)
       (e) Add the probabilities for (a), (c), and (d). [What
           must the answer be?]

2. A new instructor is assigned a General Mathematics class. At
   the end of the semester, the average of this class: x = 62.3
   for the 27 'survivors' (12 withdrew along the way). Over
   several semesters, class averages have been $\bar{x}$ = 73.1 with a
   standard deviation of 16.3. What is the probability of obtaining an average of 62.3 or less? [Let's ignore those who
   withdrew; many withdraw for personal reasons rather than academic ones and the two groups were not distinguished.]

3. Let's 'correct' our sampling from our 69 General Mathematics
   students: We took four non-overlapping samples from this
   finite population. Our means were all right: the means of
   the samples tend toward the mean of the population, but the
   standard deviation of the sample means [SIGMA($\bar{x}$) = 4.2797]
   needs an additional correction factor, namely, a multiplier:
   SQRT[(N-n)/N-1)], where N is the population size, N = 69, and
   n is the sample size, n = 10.

         SIGMA($\bar{x}$) = [SIGMA/SQRT(n)]{SQRT[(N-n)/(N-1)]}

     or 4.2797 = [SIGMA/SQRT(10)]{SQRT[(69-10)/(69-1)]}

   Find the value of the population standard deviation, SIGMA,
   predicted from this sampling. [Compare with the known value,
   SIGMA = 15.890.]

4. Ashley is concerned about the gas consumption for her car. She
   managed to keep records (only one lapse) for the past three
   months:

Date	Mileage	Gallons	Average Miles
Oct	53405	17.5	16.5
	742	17.0	18.9

	Mileage	Gallons	Average Miles
	?	17.8	
	54417	17.5	19.1
	667	13.8	18.1
	980	18.7	16.7
Nov	55189	14.0	14.9
	487	15.9	18.7
	764	16.1	17.2
	56062	18.4	16.2
	449	20.0	19.4
Dec	831	17.1	22.3
	57036	15.1	13.6
	395	18.7	19.2

Find the mean of these average miles. If you ignore the individual entries and find the average miles for the entire period: (57395 - 53116)/237.6 [miles traveled/total gallons] you'll find a considerable discrepancy. What's gone wrong?

Find the standard deviation for the mean of the average miles. If Ashley were to check prior 3-months periods and find the mean, $MU(x)$, for each such period, how would these means be distributed? What assumptions are we making? Are the assumptions valid? What questions would you want to ask before you assent?

5. Assuming the means, $MU(x)$, [#4], are normally distributed, what is the probability of obtaining a value for MU larger than 20? less than 16?

6. Find an 80% CI for the means [#4]. [Note: an 80% CI symmetric about the mean implies 'tails' totalling 20 per cent of the area, or 10 per cent each, which, in turn, implies a z-value, $z = 1.28$, marking the boundary; use Table A-4.]

Find a 90% CI for the means [#4]. What happens to the size of of the interval when we increase the rate of confidence? Explain what's happening in reasonable English.

7. To find the Confidence Intervals in #6, we used Table A-4 which may not have been strictly legitimate: we were saying, in effect, that the standard deviation for the 'sample' -- the only collection of data we own -- would hold up for the next sample, and the next, ... You get the idea. But, of course, we can't be sure. This time, repeat #6: find an 80% CI and a 90% CI, but use the t-Distribution table, Table A-5. [How many degrees of freedom?] What happens to the Confidence Intervals? Does this behavior seem rational?

8. Following good practice procedures, we make a prior decision
   that we'll be tolerant of an Error, E, of no more than 5 per
   cent. NOW, we proceed to collect our data! From prior sampling, we find that we have a standard error of s = 15.

   (i) With the allowable Error in mind, what should be our
       sample size when next we sample?

   (ii) In #4, we found a value for the standard error, s = 2.24.
        With the same value for E: 5 per cent, what should be
        sample size when next we sample? Can we trust this
        value?

   (iii) Try the standard error, s = 2.24, with a 2.5 per cent
         Error. (There's an advantage with small standard
         error!)

HYPOTHESIS TESTING FOR THE MEAN AND VARIANCE OF A POPULATION

Hypothesis Testing for the Mean: Large Sample

A natural extension of the idea of the Confidence Interval is this new idea of Hypothesis Testing. Sometimes a concept is around so long that it becomes encrusted with barnacles. Then, along comes some researcher who doesn't believe the concept at all --claims, in fact, he has data to demonstrate it's false. Are we to believe him? Is his experimental data convincing?

For example, you might walk yourself proudly into the office of your department head and tell him the good news that the results of your survey of 69 General Mathematics students shows a mean score of 72.116 and a variance of 252.4864. Your department head tells you in no uncertain terms that your sample is not representative: that his long years of experience have shown that the mean value for General Mathematics students is exactly 75. How might you justify your sample scores? One of two things has happened: your department head is correct and your sample mean is well within an acceptable range of scores, OR the accepted mean of 75 is incorrect, a new mean must be sought (or the examination be adjusted).

Your test for the Mean might be described as follows: the 'accepted' value is placed in the NULL HYPOTHESIS, the experimental value is included in the ALTERNATIVE HYPOTHESIS (also known as the RESEARCH HYPOTHESIS). Our thinking, initially, proceeds thusly: our department head believes the mean should be (has been) 75. Our experimental data seems to indicate that value may be incorrect: the true value may be larger or smaller. We set up our test:

Null Hypothesis, H(o): MU = 75

Alternative Hypothesis, H(a): MU =/ 75

What are we trying to accomplish? We either want to REJECT
our Null Hypothesis [H(o)]:   the true Mean value for General Mathematics students on this examination is NOT the accepted value, 75,
OR we FAIL TO REJECT (FTR) the Null Hypothesis: we don't have sufficient evidence to disbelieve 75 as the Mean of all General Mathematics students on this examination.   [Notice, we do NOT ACCEPT 75
as the mean; just FAIL TO REJECT; there's a significant semantic
and statistical difference.]

In statistics, nothing is absolutely certain. We decide, before we initiate the test, our degree of uncertainty. Our department head might be wrong (we'll be tactful pointing this out), or
we might be: our sample data might be misleading or need further
verification. If we were to reject the Null Hypothesis when, in
fact, it's true ('I told you so'), this is called a TYPE I error
and the probability of making such an error is a numerical value
called ALPHA. If we were to fail to reject the Null Hypothesis if
in fact, it's false (be judicious, department heads get grumpy if
crossed), this is called a TYPE II error and the probability of
making such an error is a numerical value called BETA.

P[We reject H(o) when it's true] = P(Type I error) = ALPHA

P[We fail to reject H(o) when it's false] = P(Type II error) = BETA

Now, we can't control both of these: if we diminish one the
other increases. If H(o) is true, the mean 'truly' is 75, and the
Normal curve is symmetric about this mean value. If H(o) is not
true, the mean is not 75, but rather some other value—larger or
smaller—and our Normal curve lies elsewhere: it's picked up and
moved up or down the scale. If our Mean is truly 75 and our sample
mean indicates otherwise, we're going to bray like a jackass that
the Null Hypothesis is wrong; but no one wants to be a jackass too
often. On the other hand, if we're too conservative—too afraid
to be thought a jackass—we're going to fail to reject H(o) when
we should: and others will get the glory and the publication.

We initiate a procedure: we'll set ALPHA in advance; we'll
allow ourselves some error (Type I). Customarily, we'll set ALPHA
between .01 and .1. Why not simply choose the smallest ALPHA and
proceed with it? Because a smaller ALPHA means a larger BETA: if
we diminish our probability of rejecting H(o) when it's true, we
enhance our probability of failing to reject H(o) when it's false.
If we can't decide on a significant difference between Type I or
Type II error, we'll set ALPHA = .05 (not exactly halfway, but it's
'what's done').

Before we get bogged down in trying to explain all the diffi-
culties we can get ourselves into, let's proceed with the test (and
dig ourselves out of trouble later, if we must). We need a TEST

STATISTIC that expresses our aim: we'll let H(o): MU = 75 stand if
if our sample mean, x̄ = 72.116, is not 'too different.' Conversely,
we will reject if x̄ = 72.116 is too far away from our mean, MU=75.
Standardizing, so we can use the Normal distribution table, we want

$$Z = |(X - 75)/[15.89/SQRT(69)]| > 1.96$$

Where did the figures come from? Recall that our sample variance was 252.486, and so our standard deviation is the 15.89; the
sample size was 69; we decided that we'd let ALPHA be .05, allowing
ourselves this much error. Since we're not entirely sure the mean
is truly greater than 75 or less, we'll set Z so that the region of
rejection is split between the left and right tails of the distribution, leaving .05/2 = .025 as the area in each tail. From the
table, we find Z = 1.96 for an area equal to .5 - .025 = .4750.

Now, the X we're interested in checking is X = 72.116. It
follows that

$$Z* = (72.116 - 75)/[15.89/SQRT(69)] = -1.508$$

where the Z* indicates the COMPUTED VALUE of Z.

What do we conclude? That our department head is right after
all: our figure of 72.116 isn't different enough (for ALPHA = .05)
to indicate that the mean is not 75. We FAIL TO REJECT H(o). Back
to the drawing board.

Let's reset our ALPHA. This is a dangerous (immoral) move.
We set ALPHA originally as an expression of our confidence in our
procedure and our understanding of the underlying data. To reset
it now is statistically inadmissible. So, let's do it anyway.
Suppose we allow ourselves an error of ALPHA = .1; then ALPHA/2 =
.05 and we're looking for a Z value: .5 - .05 = .4500, and from
Table A-4, Z = 1.645. If we had initially decided that the situation called for this value, we would have written

$$|(X - 75)/[15.89/SQRT(69)]| > 1.645$$

We note, with chagrin, that even allowing ourselves a maximum
Type I error, we still yet can't justify our research hypothesis.

Is there anything to be salvaged from our work? Do we turn
out the lights and go home? We did find our Z* = 1.508. From
Table A-4, for Z = 1.51, the entry reads .4345. Looking for the
area under the curve in the tail: .5 - .4345 = .0755.

This last value is called the p-VALUE for the test we've con-
cluded. We would write:

$$p = .0755$$

The p-value is the value of ALPHA at which the hypothesis test procedure changes conclusions. The rules for reporting the p-value are

reject H(o) if the p-value is small: $p < .01$

fail to reject H(o) [FTR] if the p-value is large: $p > .1$

What are we to do with a p-value of $p = .0755$, which falls betwixt? Report it! These are precisely the values that need reporting: we have failed to reject H(o) at ALPHA = .05. We have at hand -- the p-value -- a measure of our concern. Perhaps we, on some new data, or another researcher, will verify (or contradict) our conclusion, and the impetus for additional investigation might be the nagging doubt the p-value has introduced.

In fact, let's suppose it's another semester and another set of grades on, say, 65 students, with a mean of $\bar{x} = 69$ and a standard deviation, s = 15. Again, our

Null Hypothesis, H(o): MU = 75

Alternative Hypothesis, H(a): MU =/ 75

and again we conduct our test, setting ALPHA = .05. We want

$$| (X - 75)/[15/SQRT(65)] | > 1.96$$

For $\bar{x} = 69$, we compute

$$Z* = (69 - 75)/[15/SQRT(65)] = -3.225$$

This time we reject the null hypothesis: the computed value, Z*, is well within the tail (on the left). The mean value, MU =/ 75.

Well, if the mean is not 75, what is the mean value? Let's suppose (since we have no data which suggest otherwise) that the mean truly is MU = 69, and that our Normal distribution curve is centered on this value. If we were to FAIL TO REJECT the null hypothesis (fail to reject MU = 75) when, in fact, the mean is MU = 69, that is, commit a Type II error, what is the value of BETA? recall that Beta measures our FTR when the null hypothesis is false.

Where, on the X-scale of values does our assigned ALPHA value take us? From our test, X = 75 - (1.96)[15/SQRT(65)] = 75 - 3.647 = 71.35. How much area is there under the Normal distribution with a mean, MU = 69, and standard deviation, SIGMA = 15, 'above' 71.35? The computation:

$$Z = (71.35 - 69)/[15/SQRT(65)] = 1.265$$

suggests an area (Table A-4) between the mean (0) and a z-value of
1.265 of .3971 (with a bit of interpolation), and so an area of
.5 - .3971 = .1029 to the right (in the direction of our null value
of 75).   Thus

$$BETA = .1029$$

the measure of our error if we fail to reject the null (MU = 75)
when, in fact, our mean is MU = 69.

Another alternative mean value (other than 69) would create
another Beta: for each suggested alternative ... You get the idea.

This suggests another important concept: THE POWER of a statistical test, given by

$$1 - BETA = 1 - .1029 = .8971$$

where 1 - BETA = P(we reject H(o) if it is false). The power of a
test is a measure of our assurance: we're about 90 per cent sure
that the mean IS NOT 75 and IS 69.

Once again, let's suppose we select still another sample group
of students and give them the same (or a comparable) General Mathematics exam. This time, for the sake of argument, we'll say that
the mean, $\bar{x}$ = 82. (All right, who got hold of the exam?) Let's
set up our test as we did above:

$$Null\ Hypothesis,\ H(o):\ MU = 75$$

$$Alternative\ Hypothesis,\ H(a):\ MU =/\ 75$$

Setting ALPHA = .05, as we did above, our test:

$$|(X - 75)/[15/SQRT(65)]| > 1.96$$

where, for the sake of comparisons, we've again taken a sample of
size, n = 65, and assumed a standard deviation, SIGMA = 15. For
our new mean, $\bar{x}$ = 82,

$$Z* = (82 - 75)/[15/SQRT(65)] = 3.76$$

Once again, we're far out in the tail; this time on the right.
We would, once again, reject the null hypothesis: MU =/ 75. Well
then, what is the true mean? Let's suppose the mean, MU = 82. Once
again, conceive of our Normal distribution centered on this new
value, and ask for the value of BETA: what is the probability of
error if we fail to reject the null hypothesis when it's false?

As above, but this time on the right,

$$X = 75 + (1.96)[15/SQRT(65)] = 75 + 3.647 = 78.647$$

How much area is there under the Normal distribution with a mean, MU = 82, and standard deviation, SIGMA = 15, 'below' 78.647? Our analogous computation:

$$Z = (78.647 - 82)/[15/SQRT(65)] = -1.80$$

Consulting Table A-4, the area we want is .5 - .4641 = .0359, which suggests

$$BETA = .0359$$

The POWER of the statistical test, then, is 1 - BETA = .9641, giving us assurance--in this hypothetical situation--that the mean is, indeed, something other than that suggested by the null hypothesis.

Step back a moment: our computed Z* = 3.76 suggests a p-VALUE in the neighborhood of 0. Recall that we reject the null hypothesis if p is small (p < .01). We can't get much smaller!

One 'tail or two?

The hypothesis testing we've demonstrated has involved a data set for which the mean could be conceived to be either smaller or larger than that given in the null hypothesis. [Our null was H(o): MU = 75, and the alternative was H(a): MU =/ 75] And we took both tacks: the mean of one data set was less than 75, the mean of the second was larger. When both possibilities are under consideration we design our Hypothesis Test to accomodate and, naturally, we call it a TWO TAIL test of hypothesis.

Consider a situation where this might not apply: Gloria takes some readings of auto speeds on a state highway where the limit is 55 miles per hour. Her data for 16 cars were:

52	50	51	64
62	69	53	49
64	71	77	51
58	61	53	48

Gloria's contention is that the speed limit is being violated (of course, that's obvious) and that the average speed for all cars is in excess of the speed limit. Her test looks like this:

Null Hypothesis, H(o): MU = 55

Alternative Hypothesis, H(a): MU > 55

Note the Alternative Hypothesis: Gloria's only interest (recall
that H(a) is also known as the Research Hypothesis) is to demonstrate the law is being violated. Such, quite naturally, are
called ONE TAIL tests.

In our One Tail test, all the area under the Normal curve
we're going to allow for error lies either in the tail to the right
(as in Gloria's data) or in the tail to the left. (Naturally, we
have checked and feel we have reason to believe that the data are
normally distributed.) We choose our ALPHA, say, ALPHA = .05, much
as before, but now, rather than split to accomodate two regions,
each of area equal .025, all the area of error lies in the tail on
one side: for Gloria, in the tail to the right.

One more problem: what is our Test Statistic? With only 16
readings, we might feel that the z-Test is inappropriate. Let's
turn over to Table A-5 and apply the t-Test:

$$t = (x - MU)/[s/SQRT(n)]$$

where the mean of our data, x = 58.3125, and the standard deviation
s = 8.8523. From the table, t(.05,15) = 1.753. The test, then,
gives us

$$t = (58.3125 - 55)/[8.8523/SQRT(16)] = 1.4968$$

To reject the null hypothesis, we need t > t(.05,15) and fail
to demonstrate that the average highway speed of the cars in our
data set is not 55. [Interestingly, if we had chosen to proceed
with the z-Test, our computed value would have also been less than
the required 1.645, and again the test would have failed.]

How is this data to be reported? With the data Gloria has,
she cannot say the average speed is sufficiently more than the
limit to support her hypothesis, but she might legitimately note
that half the cars are over the limit, some dramatically so.

Hypothesis Testing for the Variance

Our researcher, Gloria, might do one more thing to support her
contention: analyze the variance of the data. Popular opinion
has it that speeds 'just a bit' in excess of the posted speed limit
are tolerable. If she can demonstrate that the data suggest we're
stretching tolerance to laxness, she might make a better case.

Let's initiate the analysis: how much latitude of judgment
are we to allow the highway patrol officer? We decide that speeds
in excess of 59 miles per hour are simply intolerable. Excessively
slow speeds also pose a danger on high speed highways. Let's agree

that, in deference to the officers, we will allow a deviation of some four miles per hour, but certainly no more!

Our test might appear as follows:

Null Hypothesis, H(o): SIGMA^2 = 16

Alternative Hypothesis, H(a): SIGMA^2 =/ 16

where we propose conducting a TWO TAIL test on the variance. Our test statistic is the CHI SQUARE, from Table A-6. We've already checked that our data are Normally distributed, and so feel confident that the test is applicable:

Test statistic: CHI SQUARE = [(n-1)s^2]/SIGMA^2 will suit our purposes. We'll find the interval of values for SIGMA SQUARE:

$$\frac{(n-1)s^2}{CHISQ(ALPHA/2,n-1)} < SIGMA^2 < \frac{(n-1)s^2}{CHISQ(1-ALPHA/2,n-1)}$$

From the data, n = 16 and the variance is 78.3625. From Table A-6, CHISQ(.05/2,15) = 27.4884 and CHISQ(1-.05/2,15) = 6.26214. A bit of calculation yields an interval of

27.76122 < SIGMA^2 < 187.70754

The corresponding interval for the standard deviation is

6.5392 < SIGMA < 13.7006

Have we made our case? You'd better believe it, as John Wayne might have said. Our alternative hypothesis has been borne out. The data suggest we're allowing speeds well in excess of the limit, even allowing for some laxity. If nothing more, some additional data seems called for and, for the nonce, some attention from the officers.

Problems

1. Grades on a standardized test given to entering freshmen are
   normally distributed. The mean is thought to be MU = 19.4
   with a standard deviation, SIGMA = 3.6. A new group of 60
   freshmen score somewhat higher, with a mean, x = 20.8. Conduct a test of hypothesis: let the alternative hypothesis
   be MU =/ 19.4; let the significance level, ALPHA = .05.
   State your conclusion.

2. Find the p-Value of the test in #1. Again, what conclusion is
   warranted?

3. If we assume that succeeding entering freshmen (#1) will likely
   have a mean, MU = 20.8. What is the probability of a Type II
   error? (The error committed by failing to reject the null
   hypothesis when it is indeed false). What is the POWER of
   the test?

4. A 90 per cent Confidence Interval for a set of 64 normally distributed scores ranges from a low of 36 to a high of 112. Let
   ALPHA = .10. Test the contention that the mean for these
   scores is 80 against the alternative, H(a): MU =/ 80.

5. The mean of a sample of size, n = 143, is found to be x = 12.07,
   and the standard deviation, s = 8.49. Test the hypothesis,
   H(o): MU > 14.24 against the alternative, H(a): MU < 14.24
   Let ALPHA = .05. Note that this is a ONE TAIL test.

6. From a population of 125 Calculus students, 45 are randomly
   chosen to be assigned to an experimental team-teaching task
   force. At the end of the course, a common examination shows
   the mean score for all students in the standard method of
   presentation to be MU = 73.6, while those in the experimental
   group recorded a mean score of 76.4. Standard deviation for
   the first group was SIGMA = 15.1, and for the experimental
   group was SIGMA = 13.7. Test the contention that the experimental teaching scheme shows evidence of superiority. Use
   ALPHA = .05 and a ONE TAIL test. Adjust the standard error
   for a finite population:

$$s(x) = [s/SQRT(n)]\{SQRT[(N-n)/(N-1)]\}$$

   Report the p-Value for the test. State your conclusions.

7. Using small samples in life-endangering situations is not uncommon. But small samples might also be used simply to save
   money! (How many multi-million dollar rockets would you be

willing to pay for?)   A recent test of chip life (run 'em
'til they burn out) found that the mean life span for 12
chips was equivalent to 43 months with standard deviation,
s = 2.5.   The previously expected life span had been 46
months.   Test (two-tail) with ALPHA = .05.   Is this new
batch inferior?

8. A sample of size n = 18 is drawn from an approximately normally
   distributed population of N = 200.   For the sample, x = 36.4
   and s = 8.8.   Test the null hypothesis that MU = 40.   Use
   significance level, ALPHA = .1 and a t-Test.   First, run the
   test without adjusting for finite population; second, run the
   test adjusting for finite population.   What are your conclusions in either case?

9. For the data in #8, test the null hypothesis, H(o): s > 10
   against the alternative, H(a): s < 10.   Use ALPHA = .1.

10. Repeat #9: test the null hypothesis, H(o): s > 7 against
    the alternative, H(a): s < 7.   Use ALPHA = .1.   Compare
    your results in #9 and #10.

INFERENCE PROCEDURES
FOR TWO POPULATIONS

Treatment versus Control

In the Fall semester, two classes in General Mathematics were taught. One used the standard text and syllabus; the other used an alternate text, departed from the standard lecture style of presentation, involved access to computer terminals, left the students, to some extent, to manage their own time--in other words, suggested students might gain more insight into mathematical concepts if the instructor were to act the part of 'manager' rather than 'reciter.' Both classes were given a common final examination, with results as follows:

'Treatment' Group					'Control' Group				
85	82	35	94	70	85	75	96	61	77
22	93	82	78	80	73	73	50	75	55
86	95	63	82	74	61	48	52	71	60
97	91	98	73	82	71	91	88	65	64
82	80	82	83		92	82	91	75	52

Some statistics from these two groups:

$\bar{x} = 78.708$ $\bar{x} = 71.32$

$s = 17.748$ $s = 14.31$

$s^2 = 314.998$ $s^2 = 204.81$

Do the results support--or fail to support--the contention that the alternative teaching atmosphere improves student retention of information? The approach parallels the development in Chapter 9: Choosing ALPHA = .05, we could seek a Confidence Interval:

$$P(-1.96 < z < 1.96) = .95$$

The required interval is given by:

$$P\{(\overline{x}(1)-\overline{x}(2))-1.96\,SQRT[SIGMA(1)^{\wedge}2/n(1)+SIGMA(2)^{\wedge}2/n(2)]<MU(1)-MU(2)$$

$$< (\overline{x}(1)-\overline{x}(2))+1.96\,SQRT[SIGMA(1)^{\wedge}2/n(1)+SIGMA(2)^{\wedge}2/n(2)]\}$$

The difference of our means is 78.708 - 71.320 = 7.388. The expression for the standard deviation is

$$SQRT[314.998/24 + 204.810/25] = 4.616$$

Our interval now reads:

$$P\{7.388 - 1.96(4.616) < MU(1)-MU(2) < 7.388 + 1.96(4.616)\}$$

A bit of arithmetic leaves us

$$P\{-1.659 < MU(1) - MU(2) < 16.435\}$$

Notice that the interval for the difference of the means includes the value 0, implying that, with the value, ALPHA = .05, our confidence interval does not preclude the possibility that there is quite possibly NO difference between the means of these two groups.

    With heavy hearts (we were hoping the alternative teaching atmosphere would show marked improvement in the students' response) let's proceed to a Test of Hypothesis:

    We state our hypotheses:

        Null Hypothesis, H(o): MU(1) - MU(2) = 0

        Alternative Hypothesis, H(a): MU(1) - MU(2) =/ 0

Our test statistic is:

$$z = [\overline{x}(1) - \overline{x}(2)]/SQRT[(s(1)^{\wedge}2/n(1)) + (s(2)^{\wedge}2/n(2))]$$

We have the computations done: z* = 7.388/4.616 = 1.6. As the confidence interval indicates, we fail to reject the null hypothesis:

$$1.6 < 1.96$$

    If we're to believe these results, the new teaching atmosphere yields results comparable to the standard teaching methods used heretofore, results that are not enough of an improvement to warrant radical adjustments.

    Before we trash the whole idea, let's take another look. Note that the classes were relatively small. When we had small samples

in prior data, we were cautioned to use the t-Test. If we were to
re-investigate with this in mind, our hypotheses would remain as
they were, but the test statistic now is:

$$t' = [\bar{x}(1) - \bar{x}(2)]/SQRT[(s(1)^2/n(1)) + (s(2)^2/n(2))]$$

But, this is the z-Test under a new name; the computation here is
precisely as before,

$$t'* = 1.6$$

but we have a new confidence interval to be governed by the t-statistic: t(ALPHA/2,df). Our ALPHA/2 remains as it was: ALPHA = .05
and ALPHA/2 = .025. The df figure is going to blow us away, though

$$df = \frac{[\dfrac{s(1)^2}{n(1)} + \dfrac{s(2)^2}{n(2)}]^2}{\dfrac{[s(1)^2/n(1)]^2}{n(1) - 1} + \dfrac{[s(2)^2/n(2)]^2}{n(2) - 1}}$$

Fortunately, we've done most of this computation before:

$$df = 454.428/10.286 = 44.178$$

So, for our t-Test, df = 44 [rounding down, always]. All we have
to do is look up t(.025,44). The .025 is all right, but there's no
44. Our table [Table A-5] is better than most, though. It does
give us

$$t(.025,40) = 2.021 \text{ and } t(.025,60) = 2.000$$

We could interpolate (we're desperate; t(.025,40) should do for us)
and get t(.025,44) = 2.017. Then the Confidence Interval becomes:

$$P[7.388 - 2.017(4.616) < MU(1) - MU(2) < 7.388 + 2.017(4.616)]$$

$$= P[7.388 - 9.3105 < MU(1) - MU(2) < 7.388 + 9.3105]$$

$$= P[-1.9225 < MU(1) - MU(2) < 16.6985] > .95$$

If we were chagrined before, we're mortified now. Our interval again includes the 0 value, and again, we can't preclude the
distinct possibility that there is no difference between our means:
that we cannot reject the null hypothesis. All this does is verify
our premonitions: our t' = 2.017 and our computed t'* = 1.6, so

$$t'* < t'$$

What shall we do? Shall we just drag our teddybear home and forget all about it?

There's one more consideration: it's just possible that the sample variances are not all that different: that in our preceding tests we've placed too much stress on their difference, and therefore, biased our results in favor of the null hypothesis. How would we know? Previous experience might help: this time, our 'treatment' group had the larger variance; is it just possible that prior samplings diminished the difference--or even reversed this difference? what's to prevent the variance of the 'control' group from being the larger?

To answer our own rhetorical questions: nothing, it seems, prevents. Let's say, in defense of our procedures, that educational experiments are almost impossible to replicate. People aren't white mice. But like results in similar experiments are comparable to like judgments from the Supreme Court: like judgments in similar cases build precedents.

Having made our apologies, let's do what we can to obviate this possible skewing by considering POOLED SAMPLE VARIANCE. The statistic for the Pooled Sample Variance is

$$s(p)^2 = [(n(1) - 1)s(1)^2+(n(2) - 1)s(2)^2]/[n(1) + n(2) - 2]$$

so, for our two samples

$$s(p)^2 = [(23)(314.998) + (24)(204.810)]/[24 + 25 - 2]$$

$$= 12160.394/47 = 258.732$$

Our test statistic is

$$t = [\bar{x}(1) - \bar{x}(2)]/\{s(p)SQRT[(1/n(1) + 1/n(2))]\}$$

which gives us

$$t = [78.708 - 71.320]/\{(258.732)SQRT[(1/24 + 1/25)]\}$$

$$= 7.388/(258.732)(.285774) = 7.388/73.939 = .1$$

Our Confidence Interval for this Pooled Variance looks like

$$P\{(\bar{x}(1) - \bar{x}(2)) - t(ALPHA/2,df(s(p))SQRT[(1/n(1) + 1/n(2))] <$$

$$MU(1) - MU(2) <$$

$$(\bar{x}(1) - \bar{x}(2) + t(ALPHA/2,df(s(p))SQRT[(1/n(1) + 1/n(2))]\} = .95$$

With the figures for our two classes, the computation is

P[7.388 - 2.014(.286) < MU(1) - MU(2) < 7.388 + 2.014(.286)] = .95

or P[6.812 < MU(1) - MU(2) < 7.964] = .95

What a difference the pooling of the sample variance makes! As our hypothesis test would verify, we have ample reason to be pleased with our experimental results.

One warning: we don't want to leave you with the impression that we keep manipulating the data until we get the result we want. Each new approach was logically justified: we abandoned the z-Test in favor of the t-Test because of the size of the samples; we moved to the Pooled Sample Variance on the conviction that the variances of our particular two groups did not reflect accurately our prior expectations regarding classes of students in General Mathematics. Our 'expectations' should be supported by prior data. If we have no prior data and move to a Pooled Sample Variance--and reject the null hypothesis--we would want to report precisely what we've done and, given opportunity, verify by sampling again under similar conditions. In a living, rather than a pedigogical, situation, we would use the z-Test for large samples, the t-Test when the differences of sample variances are significant, and Pooled Variance when we know the difference, if not compensated for, would bias our results.

Pretest-Postest

The preceding 'experiment' was analyzed on the assumption that the groups were chosen at random, that we have INDEPENDENCE. That elusive quality, independence, is seldom truly achieved. Certainly in the assignment of classes of students we can hardly claim to use random choice. Students have some rights!

Consider medical experiments: volunteers are often asked to undergo treatment or serve as controls. Are these volunteers repre sentative of the population or are they some sort of 'special' kind of people?

Experimenters do all they can to obviate the effects that might influence independence, of course.

One way is to admit defeat: to test DEPENDENT samples. We pair individuals that are as much alike as we can make them. Or we test the SAME individual once and again: a PRETEST and POSTEST.

Consider once again our class of students in General Mathematics. Each student (with one exception) was given a Pretest to gauge his prospects of success in the course: will the student complete the course successfully, or should he be asked to take remedial work in preparation? Since many students withdraw in discouragement, the need for such a Pretest seems obvious. The question remains: is the Pretest a valid predictor of student success?

Paired Pretest-Postest scores are given below for our 'Treatment' class:

| ------- | ------- | ------- | ------- | ------- |
70 22	87 93	83 82	70 78	73 80
77 86	90 95	77 63	77 82	77 74
90 97	80 91	90 98	77 73	80 82
83 82	73 80	70 82	73 83	
97 82	77 35	93 94	77 70	

The Postest-Pretest differences are:

-48	6	-1	8	7
9	5	-14	5	-3
7	11	8	-4	2
-1	7	12	10	
-15	-42	1	-7	

Some statistics for these differences are

$$\text{The mean, } \bar{d} = -1.6087$$

$$\text{The standard deviation, } s(d) = 15.5468$$

$$\text{The variance, } s(d)^2 = 241.703557$$

The t-Statistic, then, is $t(d) = -1.6087/[15.5468/\text{SQRT } 23] = -.496$.

Our Confidence Interval, then, is

$$P\{-1.6087 - (2.074)[15.5468/\text{SQRT } 23] < \text{MU(Postest)}-\text{MU(Pretest)} <$$

$$-1.6087 + (2.074)[15.5468/\text{SQRT } 23]\} = .95$$

where $t(.025,22) = 2.074$. So

$$P\{-8.332 < \text{MU(Postest)}-\text{MU(Pretest)} < 5.115\}$$

indicating that we have reason to believe that the Pretest is a valid measure of a student's prospects of success: again, the zero value is included in our interval. And a test of hypotheses would verify.

Notice that we have tested the DIFFERENCES of two DEPENDENT scores: scores obtained as pairs, in this case, from the same

individual (and, hence, obviously not independent). Notice, too,
that while we have reason to be satisfied with the test and might
continue to use it, the test doesn't work for everyone. There are
some monstrous differences: there's a -48 and a -42, for example.
What went wrong? Is the Pretest at fault? should it have anticipated these failures?

Life's like that: these students might have fallen ill, been
beset with personal problems, been unresponsive to the instructor,
hated math (no!), or who knows what. Our t-Test is only a broad in
ference, not a predictor of individual response. This Pretest seems
to work, our t-Test says. Our t-Test does not say that the results
will be universally satisfying, nor that perhaps another Pretest
might indeed work even better as a predictor.

Comparing variances

When we moved to pool variances in our work on Treatment and
Control groups, we waved our arms rather vigorously trying to justify our gut feeling that the variances of the two groups were,
despite appearances, not significantly different. We cited one
possibility: prior testing had so indicated. Trouble is, there
had been no prior testing to consult. The very fact that we were
successful in demonstrating the desired rejection of the null hypo-
thesis--when we were unable to do so in the z-Test and the standard
t-Test--makes the 'manipulation' seem even more suspicious.

Fortunately, there is a reliable statistical measure to compare variances of normal populations: the RATIO of sample variances
follows an F DISTRIBUTION. Table A-7 gives us the necessary information.

$$F = s(1)^2/s(2)^2$$

Our hypothesis test would appear, for a two-tail test, as

Null Hypothesis, H(o): SIGMA(1) = SIGMA(2)

Alternative Hypothesis, H(1): SIGMA(1) =/ SIGMA(2)

where we're considering standard deviations rather than variances
but with the same effect.

Our computed F-value, then, is

$$F* = 314.998/204.810 = 1.538$$

The choices of SIGMA(1)^2 = 314.998 and SIGMA(2)^2 = 204.810 were fortuitous: no matter how the samples are labelled, we'll ALWAYS place the larger variance in the numerator and the smaller in the denominator, to take advantage of the nature of the F-distribution, which, you'll note from the table, is skewed to the right.

Now, to the test: we're going to need degrees of freedom again, just as we did for the t-Test:

df for SIGMA(1)^2 = NU(1) = n(1) - 1 = 24 - 1 = 23

df for SIGMA(2)^2 = NU(2) = n(2) - 1 = 25 - 1 = 24

Since ALPHA/2 = .025, we'll consult Table A-7(c) to find a value for

F[.025,23,24] = 2.27

where the parentheses give us the sequence of values for ALPHA/2, NU(1) and NU(2). NU(1), the NUMERATOR degrees of freedom, is given by the columns of the table, while NU(2), the denominator degrees of freedom, is given by the rows. There's one fly in the ointment: the Numerator degrees of freedom skip from 20 to 24; we've chosen to use the column headed 24, since it's closest to our desired 23. The 'true' F value would be a wee bit larger (notice that the value under the column headed 20 is given as 2.33). If this is critical to our test, we might be a bit hesistant to report it with any degree of confidence.

What does the test tell us? Our computed F* < F; that is

1.538 < 2.27

We would reject the null hypothesis if F* > F. Since it is NOT we FAIL TO REJECT, meaning that the variances for our two classes can be taken to be, for statistical purposes, equal -- and the POOLED SAMPLE VARIANCES approach is legitimized.

Establishing a Confidence Interval for the ratio of the variances is a bit tricky since the F-distribution is not symmetric We have an F-value for the UPPER tail of the distribution, namely, 2.27. We need an F-value for the LOWER tail of the distribution, and, for us, this is going to be the reciprocal: 1/2.27 = .4405.

But it's not that easy: for samples of unequal size (ours weren't equal, but the table 'forced' us to use NU(1) = NU(2) = 24) we would take the reciprocal of

F[ALPHA/2, NU(2), NU(1)]

Notice that NU(1) and NU(2) are switched. Now, LOWER and UPPER limits to the Confidence Interval are given by

$$\frac{s(1)^\wedge 2/s(2)^\wedge 2}{F(U)} \quad \text{and} \quad \frac{s(1)^\wedge 2/s(2)^\wedge 2}{F(L)}$$

where   F(U) = F[ALPHA/2, NU(1), NU(2)]

and   F(L) = F[ALPHA/2, NU(2), NU(1)]

Our Confidence Interval, then, reads

$$\frac{1.538}{2.27} < \frac{SIGMA(1)^\wedge 2}{SIGMA(2)^\wedge 2} < \frac{1.538}{.4405}$$

or, finally, that

$$.6775 < SIGMA(1)^\wedge 2/SIGMA(2)^\wedge 2 < 3.491$$

which verifies what we knew: that the variance of the Treatment group (314.998) is larger than the variance found for the Control group (204.81), but, as the hypothesis test indicates, not enough larger to preclude use of the Pooled Sample Variance. Notice that the lower inequality includes 1, implying that it's entirely possible the two variances are equal.

Problems

1. Two independent samples are taken with results:

	n	$\bar{x}$	s
Sample 1	45	28.3	4.3
Sample 2	40	25.4	5.1

a) Construct a 95 per cent Confidence Interval for MU(1)-MU(2)

b) Find n if Maximum Error, E = 2 and a 99 per cent Confidence Interval is requested.

c) Conduct a Test of Hypotheses. Let H(o): MU(1) = MU(2) and H(a): MU(1) =/ MU(2). Use ALPHA = .05. State your conclusion.

d) What is the p-Value for the test in (c)?

e) Suppose both Sample 1 and Sample 2 were of size, n = 20. Test the hypotheses in (c) once again, using the z-Test, with ALPHA = .05. State your conclusion. Does it agree with the conclusion in (c)?

f) Construct a 99 per cent Confidence Interval [see (b)] for MU(1) - MU(2). Is the interval here larger or smaller than the interval for (a)? Explain.

g) Repeat (e) using the t-Test. Note that n < 30 for each sample, so that we could argue that the z-Test is not applicable. What is your conclusion?

h) If we assume equal variances and pool, test again at ALPHA = .05. Use n(1) = n(2) = 20. Find the appropriate Confidence Interval. Can we reject the null hypothesis?

i) Apply the F-Test to the sample variances. Test for

$$SIGMA(1) = SIGMA(2)$$

at ALPHA = .05, n(1) = 45, n(2) = 40.

j) Find a 95 per cent Confidence Interval for

$$SIGMA(2)^2/SIGMA(1)^2$$

Do we preclude the possibility that SIGMA(1)=SIGMA(2)?

k) Repeat (i) and (j) for n(1) = n(2) = 20. Again, do we
   preclude the possibility that SIGMA(1) = SIGMA(2)?

2. A second class in General Mathematics was given a Pretest. The
   Pretest and Postest scores for each student are as follows:

-------		-------		-------		-------	
90	85	83	73	77	52	24	65
77	73	70	48	73	88	80	75
70	61	100	91	90	91	93	77
100	71	87	82	73	61	83	55
97	92	93	96	90	75	73	60
87	75	77	50	70	71	77	64
						83	52

Is the Pretest a reliable predictor of success in the course,
as represented by the Postest score?

ESTIMATION AND TESTING
FOR POPULATION
PROPORTIONS

You've noted, I'm sure, that many survey questions are written to be answered Yes or No. Would you vote for candidate Wintergroin for President? Do you believe the national speed limit should be raised to 65 miles per hour? (That one's been taken care of.) Should 18-year-olds be allowed in bars serving liquor? (That one should be accompanied by a second question: How old are you?)

This chapter addresses questions of this sort with some heavy stipulations. If we let p equal the probability the question is answered in the affirmative, then p must remain constant from trial to trial. We call these BERNOULLI trials. (Bernoulli is a famous Swiss family which has contributed to mathematics for generations from the 18th century on.) If p varies from trial to trial--or if independence breaks down--we may be dealing with a Markov Chain or some other case of dependence. But that's another bedtime story.

Estimation and Confidence Intervals for a Population Proportion

A Pretest is given an incoming group of General Mathematics students. (Remember them?) The results (number correct out of 30) look this this:

16	22	23	27	18	27	22	26	21	24
23	23	23	23	26	18	23	23	22	26
27	25	22	21	28	21	18	25	27	22
25	18	28	30	17	16	18	21	25	15
20	27	19	29	17	24	12	19	17	26
26	20	20	26	23	12	25	14	19	20
27	21	23	19	20	24	24	13	21	22
10	28	24	21	27	28	21	15	24	19
24	21	11	30	22	25	26	24	25	13

Since the university requires at least one course in Mathematics, the General Mathematics course is the one advised by many counsellors to fill the requirement and, by the way, give students an introduction to probability and statistics (!) This, in turn, is a concern to those teaching the course. The Pretest is designed to assure success as best we may; those failing to pass are aided to obtain assistance. The Pretest is a classical Bernoulli trial: pass-or-fail. The trials àre independent: the exams are proctored to assure that they be. The requirement is the same for all those taking the exam: a passing grade is 70 per cent: 21 correct out of 30.

The sample proportion of 'success' - those passing the Pretest - $\hat{p}$ (we read this "p hat") is an UNBIASED estimator of the population mean, MU. [Unbiased means that a series of successive trials will yield sample proportions that have MU as their mean.] Since 61 of the 90 students passed, our

$$\hat{p} = .68$$

What do we know--what can we expect--about the entire 'population,' all students who might take the Pretest?

We want a Confidence Interval for p, the Population mean, with $\hat{p}$, the Sample mean, as an estimator. Can we use what we know? Can we use the z-Test? The answer is Yes (or we wouldn't have brought it up) provided that, as a sort of 'rule of thumb,'

$$np > 5 \text{ and } n(1-p) > 5$$

For our data, $np = 90(.68) = 61$, and $n(1-p) = 29$, so we seem to be in no danger. Our test statistic, then, is

$$Z = (\hat{p} - p)/SQRT[p(1-p)/n]$$

where the denominator is the Standard deviation or Standard error. Thus, a 95 per cent Confidence Interval for p, the population mean, would appear as

$$P\{\hat{p} - 1.96SQRT[p(1-p)/n] < p < \hat{p} + 1.96SQRT[p(1-p)/n]\} = .95$$

which, with our value for $\hat{p}$, gives us

$$P\{.68-1.96SQRT[(.68)(.32)/90] < p < .68+1.96SQRT[(.68)(.32)/90]\}$$

$$= P\{.68-1.96(.049) < p < .68+1.96(.049)\}$$

$$= P\{.68-.09655 < p < .68+.09655\}$$

$$= P\{.58 < p < .78\}$$

Thus, with 95 per cent confidence, we are assured the true population mean lies between values .58 and .78.   We've allowed an error

$$E = Z(ALPHA/2)SQRT[p(1-p)/n] = 1.96SQRT[(.68)(.32)/90 = .09655$$

If we felt that the error allowed was too large, what could we do? We might well feel that passing no more than 68 per cent of incoming General Mathematics students was already a bit alarming. If, from the interval, we see that it's entirely possible we're going to see perhaps as many as 40 per cent fail, we'd want to revise our Pretest, adjust our thinking, send out an alarm,... who knows what? To allow no more than a 3 per cent error, we could test using a larger group of students. How many? Solving the error equation for n, we would have

$$n = [Z(ALPHA/2)]^2[p(1-p)]/E^2$$

$$or, \; n = [1.96]^2[(.68)(.32)]/[.03^2] = 928.8$$

that is, a sample size of n = 929. For large, nation-wide tests, this might be possible. But, samples this size are just not feasible. The entire local population of General Mathematics students may not be so large. What would you do?

The failure rate was reduced by half by allowing retesting: review classes were held and new versions of the 30-question Pretest administered with the result that 14 of the 29 in this group passed the retest in its first or second administration.

The new sample proportion of success became

$$\hat{p} = 75/90 = .83$$

With this new sample mean, the Confidence Interval becomes

$$P\{.83-1.96SQRT[(.83)(.17)/90] < p < .83+1.96SQRT[(.83)(.17)/90]\}$$

$$= P\{.756 < p < .910\}$$

Better? It certainly looks better.

Did we do these students a favor by coaching and administering a retest once and again? Of our 29, just 8 finally passed the course; 21 failed the course or failed to complete the course. Was the rescue effort worth it? That's what we pay department chairmen to decide! Just in case it's worrying you: of those who passed the Pretest on the first try, 59 per cent passed the course. The 8 of our original 29 who were coached through the Pretest and were, therefore, allowed to try the course represent just 27.6 per cent success.

Comparing Two Population Proportions

Our 90 students were actually divided into three classes and taught by three different instructors. A glance at one of these classes seems to indicate the students were considerably less successful than the students in the other two classes. Let's do some analysis. We'll list the scores on the final exam in the three classes:

I					II					III			
85	82	35	94	70	85	75	96	61	77	68	67	76	61
22	93	82	78	80	73	73	50	75	55	70	42	58	85
86	95	63	82	74	61	48	52	71	60	54	59	60	98
97	91	98	73	74	71	91	88	65	64	57	65	72	52
82	80	82	83		92	82	91	75	52	70	73	67	53

If we were, typically, to assign a failing grade to scores below 60, we'd have two failures in class I, five in class II, and seven in class III. We may find it alarming that the third class with 20 students has as many failing grades as the other two classes, with a total of 49 students, combined.

If we were to consider just two Classes: the first combining I and II, and the second consisting of III, our hypotheses would be

Null hypothesis, H(o): p(I & II) = p(III)

Alternative hypothesis, H(a): p(I & II) > p(III)

Is a test for Population Proportion valid? A quick check tells us

n(I & II)p(I & II) = 42 and n(III)p(III) = 13

Both values are large enough (greater than 5) to allow us some breathing room.

We choose ALPHA = .05, a fairly neutral value favoring neither class, neither I & II nor III.

Our test statistic, then, is the usual Z-value:

$$Z = \frac{p(I\ \&\ II) - p(III)}{\sqrt{\dfrac{p(I\ \&\ II)(1 - p(I\ \&\ II))}{n(I\ \&\ II)} + \dfrac{p(III)(1 - p(III))}{n(III)}}}$$

With our data,

$$Z* = \frac{42/49 - 13/20}{SQRT\left[\dfrac{(42/49)(7/49)}{49} + \dfrac{(13/20)(7/20)}{20}\right]} = 1.759$$

Since, Z(ALPHA) = 1.645 for our ONE-TAIL Test, and Z* > Z, we have justification in our rejection of the Null Hypothesis: we do indeed have reason to believe that Class III has scored significantly below classes I & II.

The corresponding confidence interval, however, reveals reason for caution: a 90% C.I. on the difference between the two means looks like this:

$$\left(\frac{42}{49} - \frac{13}{20}\right) - 1.645\left\{SQRT\left[\frac{\frac{42}{49}(1 - \frac{42}{49})}{49} + \frac{\frac{13}{20}(1 - \frac{13}{20})}{20}\right]\right\} < p(I \& II) - p(III)$$

& Te

$$< \left(\frac{42}{49} - \frac{13}{20}\right) + 1.645\left\{SQRT\left[\frac{\frac{42}{49}(1 - \frac{42}{49})}{49} + \frac{\frac{13}{20}(1 - \frac{13}{20})}{20}\right]\right\}$$

$$= [.20714 - 1.645(.1178)] < p(I \& II) - p(III)$$

$$< .20714 + 1.645(.1178)$$

$$= .20714 - .19376 < p(I \& II) - p(III) < .20714 + .19376$$

$$.01338 < p(I \& II) - p(III) < .4009$$

which puts our difference perilously in view of zero.

The p-Value for the test (don't confuse this 'p' with the p of the population proportion), for our computed Z-value of 1.759 is .039, from which we infer that the result is highly dependent on our choice of ALPHA.

We still have a bit of tidying to do. We assumed a certain tolerance of error, as specified by our choice of Z(ALPHA), for our one-tail test, of 1.645. Unfortunately, such a grand gesture is not without cost: to compensate, we have to select a sample size -- or sizes, since we're comparing two populations -- that is commensurate with our error tolerance.

If we were legitimately sampling and drawing inferences, we would choose sample sizes, n(1) and n(2), for our two populations as follows:

$$n(1) = \frac{Z(ALPHA/2)(A + B)}{E^2} \quad \text{and} \quad n(2) = \frac{Z(ALPHA/2)(B + C)}{E^2}$$

where our presumed - preassigned - error was .10, and values for

$$A = p(1)[1 - p(1)] \qquad B = SQRT\{p(1)p(2)[1 - p(1)]\{1 - p(2)]\}$$

$$\text{and} \qquad C = p(2)[1 - p(2)]$$

If we were truly to do so, our sample sizes would then be

$$n(I \& II) = (1.645)^2[.123 + .167]/(.1)^2 = 78.346$$

$$n(III) = (1.645)^2[.167 + .228]/(.1)^2 = 106.746$$

In other words, sample sizes of 79 and 107, respectively. Well, we've done no such thing: our class sizes were pre-ordained.

We've used Z(ALPHA) rather than Z(ALPHA/2) since we were interested in a ONE-TAIL Test.

The error we've actually tolerated is

$$E = Z(ALPHA)SQRT[\frac{p(I \& II)(1 - p(I \& II))}{n(I \& II)} + \frac{p(III)(1 - p(III))}{n(III)}]$$

or

$$E = .19376$$

Our Confidence Interval then looks like $(\frac{42}{49} - \frac{13}{20})$ +/- .19376, or (.01338, .40094). The lower limit of the interval looks perilously close to zero! Are we still so very certain of our results? Before we lay heads on the chopping block, we should sample again. No one sample should motivate us toward irreversible actions.

One more bit of tidying: we've been working with samples of such size that the Z-Test was applicable. Proportions testing is possible with smaller samples, and we'll address this question in the Problems set.

Problems

1. Our Pretest students broke down in typical Bernoulli Trial fashion into 'pass' and 'no-pass' groups: 36 passed the course of the 61 who passed the Pretest on the first try; 8 passed the course of the 29 who were coached and allowed two more tries at the Pretest. Totalling, 44 of the original 90 passed the course. Find a confidence interval for the probability of passing the course [ALPHA = .05] if this strategy is continued. Can we use the Z-test?

2. You may not like the looks of the results in #1. The probability of successfully passing the course for any incoming group of students looks alarmingly small. Look again: of the original 90, just 75 passed the Pretest either on the first or succeeding tries. Now: 44 of these 75 (NOT of the original 90) passed the course. With this new viewpoint, find a confidence interval for the probability of passing the course [again, ALPHA = .05] if this strategy is continued. Can we still use the Z-test?

3. Comment on the results in #1 and #2. [Figures in statistics are stillborn without meaningful (and truthful!) interpretation.]

4. You are overwhelmed by a mass of data (90 scores on the Pretest to analyze!). [You may be less than overwhelmed, but let's pretend.] You decide to randomly select from among the given scores, and choose just 12 scores to represent the data. Using a random number generator, we select the following scores:

#:	44	69	79	66	6	82	22	39	62	34	85	73
Score:	27	14	21	25	26	24	28	28	21	19	15	21

   Using just these scores, find a 95% C.I. on p, the proportion of students passing the Pretest. Since the Z-test will no longer apply (check!), we take advantage of Table A-8 for n = 12, ALPHA = .05. Compare this result with the result using all 90 scores.

5. If you have a random number generator on your calculator (or a CRC Handbook or somesuch), repeat #4. You'll find (we hope) that your results are significantly different.

6. For sample proportion, $\hat{p}$ = .45, and sample size, n = 150, find
   a) a 95% C.I. for p, the population proportion, and b) the
   maximum error.

7. For sample proportion, $\hat{p}$ = .45, and sample size, n = 150, as in
   #6, find a) a 99% C.I. for p, and b) a 90% C.I. for p.
   Explain the three results: #6a, #7a, and #7b.

8. Repeat #6: again, sample proportion, $\hat{p}$ = .45, but this time with
   sample size, n = 15. Again, find a 95% C.I. What is the
   (not unexpected) effect of the drastic reduction in sample
   size?

ANALYSIS OF VARIANCE

Let's consider our two classes of General Mathematics students once more, but from a novel point of view. To start, let's
randomly sample five members from our first grouping (classes I
and II), and sample another five from our second grouping (class
III). Our two samples of Final Test scores are:

```
        I & II                III
        ------                ---

          86                   57
          91                   76
          82                   58
          73                   61
          77                   70
         ---                  ---
         409                  322
```

From these we compute the following Sums of Squares, as the
beginning of our ANOVA: Analysis of Variance, another way to
determine the difference of two means.

$$SS(factor) = \left[\frac{T(1)^2}{n(1)} + \frac{T(2)^2}{n(2)}\right] - \frac{T^2}{n}$$

where T(1) and T(2) are the total scores from I & II and III, respectively, n(1) and n(2) are the total number of scores from I & II
and III, T is the total of all (10) scores, and n is the total number of scores. We are defining 'factor' for our analysis as 'class'

A bit of plug and chug yields the figures:

$$SS(factor) = [\frac{(409)^2}{5} + \frac{(322)^2}{5}] - \frac{(731)^2}{10} = 756.9$$

A second of our Sums of Squares is

$$SS(total) = SUM(x^2) - \frac{T^2}{n}$$

where, once more, x represents the individual scores (10 in all), and the T is our total of all scores. Doing the arithmetic,

$$SS(total) = 54669 - \frac{(731)^2}{10} = 1232.9$$

The third (last!) of our Sums of Squares is

$$SS(error) = SS(total) - SS(factor)$$

which becomes $= 1232.9 - 756.9 = 476.0$

To complete the test, we need just two more figures, the

$$MS(factor) = SS(factor)/df(factor)$$

and $MS(error) = SS(error)/df(error)$

where MS is MEAN SQUARE, df(factor) = number of factors (classes)-1 = 2-1 = 1, and df(error) = n(1) + n(2) - 2 = 5 + 5 - 2 = 8. So our

$$MS(factor) = 756.9/1 = 756.9$$

and $MS(error) = 476/8 = 59.5$

Our test is the F-Test, F = MS(factor)/MS(error). If we had previously set ALPHA = .10, then, from Table A-7, the value for

$$F(.1,1,8) = 3.46$$

where we have 1 degree of freedom for the numerator: MS(factor), and 8 degrees of freedom for the denominator: MS(error).

Our test, then, is

$$F* = 756.9/59.5 = 12.72$$

Now, since F* > F, we reject the null hypothesis that the means of our two samples are equal. Indeed, it seems that the scores in classes I & II are higher than those in III, just as in Chapter 11 we found that the proportion of failures in class III were significantly higher than those in I & II.

To try to keep track of all the figures, most people find it convenient to set up an ANOVA TABLE, somewhat as here:

Source	df	SS	MS	F
Factor	1	756.9	756.9	756.9
Error	8	476.0	59.5	----- = 12.72
Total	9	1220.9		59.5

To obtain our figures, and conduct our test, we sampled from the two classes, randomly selecting five from classes I & II and five from class III. Obviously, the results could very well have been different with another sampling. With statistical processes, we are always subject to chance.

The 'populations' are not so very large: taking all the data from classes I & II and from class III, the computations would look like:

$$SS(factor) = \left[\frac{(3664)^2}{49} + \frac{(1307)^2}{20}\right] - \frac{(4971)^2}{69} = 1261.789$$

$$SS(total) = 375109 - \frac{(4971)^2}{69} = 16980.870$$

$$SS(error) = 16980.870 - 1261.789 = 15719.081$$

The ANOVA TABLE then appears this way:

Source	df	SS	MS	F
Factor	1	1261.789	1261.789	5.38
Error	67	15719.081	234.613	
Total	68	16980.870		

while, from Table A-7, $F(.1,1,68) = 2.78$. Since $F^* > F$, once more, we reject our implied Null hypothesis and, once more, claim that the means of our two factors (classes) are indeed unequal.

One-factor ANOVA: More than Two Means

The strength of the Analysis of Variance technique is its adaptability. With it, we need not restrict our attention to only two means. By a simple and natural extension, we can write the following:

$$SS(factor) = [\frac{T(1)^2}{n(1)} + \frac{T(2)^2}{n(2)} + \frac{T(3)^2}{n(3)}] - \frac{T^2}{n}$$

for the consideration of three sample sets with degrees of freedom, $df = 3 - 1 = 2$. You can see the obvious extension to k sample sets with $df = k - 1$. The others: SS(total) and SS(error) remain as we have specified them with, as might be expected, $df(total) = n - 1$ and $df(error) = n - k$. The Mean Square values, MS(factor) and MS(error) are obtained in the same way.

Let's take one more look at our three General Mathematics classes (why not!), but this time with this new feeling of power in our hands.

For our three factors (classes), $T(1) = 1881$, $T(2) = 1763$, and $T(3) = 1307$, so that

$$SS(factor) = [\frac{(1881)^2}{24} + \frac{(1783)^2}{25} + \frac{(1307)^2}{20}] - \frac{(4971)^2}{69}$$

$$= 1871.25$$

$$SS(total) = SUM(x^2) - \frac{T^2}{n} = 375109 - 358128.13 = 16980.87$$

and so $SS(error) = 16980.87 - 1871.25 = 15109.62$

Trotting right along,

$$MS(factor) = 1871.25/2 = 935.625$$

and $$MS(error) = 15109.62/66 = 228.934$$

Our computed F-value, then, is

$$F* = 935.625/228.934 = 4.09$$

Meanwhile, from the table, $F(.1,2,66) = 2.38$, and so $F* > F$, and (guess what?) we reject our inferred null: these means are not equal.

There's a fly in the ointment, however. If we had embarked upon this last test first, we would not know precisely where the inequality lay. This extension to three factors (classes) does not tell us where to place blame. Further analysis would have to be conducted.

We have still another fly in the myrrh: to conduct the test

we inferred that (i) the samples were obtained randomly and independently, (ii) these scores are normally distributed, and (iii)
their variances are not too different. At least (i) is highly
suspect: these classes came to us, not by our random choosing,
but by the 'luck of registration.' The other stipulations could
be checked.

Confidence Intervals for One-factor ANOVA

Analogous to prior tests, we can specify a confidence interval
for our test. We've done most of the work required. As we stated,
we're assuming the variances of the factors (classes) are not too
different, but just to keep things honest, we'll use a

POOLED VARIANCE, $s^2 = SS(error)/df(error)$

For example, a (1 - ALPHA)100% C.I. for the mean of the first
class, MU(1), with ALPHA = .05, would appear so:

The first class (I) has mean, MU = 78.375. The pooled value
for variance is

$$s(p)^2 = 15109.62/66 = 228.934$$

so that, with t(.025,66) = 2, our confidence interval becomes

$$78.375 - (2)SQRT(228.934/24) < MU < 78.375 + (2)SQRT(228.934/24)$$

$$75.289 < MU < 81.464$$

Similar bounds on the means for classes II and III could be
found.

Similarly, a (1 - ALPHA)100% C.I. for the DIFFERENCE OF MEANS
can be specified. For example, class I has mean, MU(1) = 78.375
and class III as mean, MU(3) = 65.35. If we again let ALPHA = .05,
the expression for our confidence interval appears as

$$(78.375-65.35) - (2)(15.13)SQRT[\frac{1}{24} + \frac{1}{20}] < MU(1) - MU(3) <$$

$$(78.375-65.35) + (2)(15.13)SQRT[\frac{1}{24} + \frac{1}{20}]$$

$$13.025 - 9.16 < MU(1) - MU(3) < 13.025 + 9.16$$

$$3.86 < MU(1) - MU(3) < 22.19$$

which verifies our suspicions that the means of the two classes are
unequal. Once again, t(.025,66) = 2, s(p) = 15.13, and the respec-
tive class sizes are 24 and 20.

Once again, class comparisons for MU(1)-MU(2) and MU(2)-MU(3)
would contribute insight to our computed F* = 4.09, which, if you
recall, told us the means were significantly different, but didn't
tell us which of the three factors, classes I, II, or III, was
causing the difficulty.

Paired samples

What if our data were not independent but were, quite obviously, dependent? If, for example, we were to obtain a pair of scores
from each individual in our study, the scores would be dependent
and fail to fulfill one of our stipulations: data values were to
be obtained randomly and independently, from normal populations,
with common variance. With a bit of adjustment our ANOVA test will
care for these pairs (or other BLOCKS of whatever size) quite well.

Our 3-Factor, 2-Block data appears as

	I				II				III		
70	22	90	98	90	85	73	88	80	68	73	55
77	86	70	82	77	73	90	91	70	70	80	60
90	97	93	94	100	71	73	61	77	57	80	72
83	82	70	78	97	92	90	75	83	70	80	67
97	82	77	82	87	75	70	71	70	67	87	61
87	93	77	73	83	73	80	65	87	42	73	85
90	95	73	83	70	48	80	75	70	59	87	98
80	91	77	70	100	91	93	77	90	65	73	52
73	80	73	80	87	82	83	55	83	73	87	53
77	85	77	74	93	96	73	60	77	76		
83	82	80	82	73	50	77	64				
77	63			77	52	83	52				
				70	61						

We still have a bit of a problem. Not only are our factors, the
three classes rather cumbersome, but, worse, they're not of the
same size. To make the computations bearable, let's randomly
sample from our three factors, using a random number generator,
and obtain the following samples, hoping fondly that the selection
we make blindly represents the data in the original set.

Our new data set, then, is the following:

I		II		III	
83	82	77	52	77	57
77	70	90	75	80	60
93	94	87	75	87	98
70	78	77	73	90	65
77	85	77	78	70	70

The corresponding Sums of Squares are computed as

$$SS(factor) = \frac{1}{b}[T(1)^2 + T(2)^2 + T(3)^2] - \frac{T^2}{bk}$$

where b = the number of blocks = 15, and where k = the number of factors = 3, the three classes, just as before. A bit of tedious arithmetic:

$$SS(factor) = 1/15[809^2 + 761^2 + 754^2] - [2324^2]/(15)(3)$$

$$= 1/15[1802118] - [5400976]/45$$

$$= 120141.20 - 120021.69 = 119.51$$

You notice that the Factor Sum of Squares totals the entries in each Block (pair), adds and squares for $T(i)^2$, i = 1,2,3, thus rubbing out (gangster fashion) the block effect.

Now, let's put the block effect back in. We want

$$SS(blocks) = \frac{1}{k}[S(1)^2 + S(2)^2 + ... + S(15)^2] - \frac{T^2}{bk}$$

where everything is as before and the new kid on the block is the S(i) values, the sums of the blocks. For us, then,

$$SS(blocks) = 1/3[131951 + 116635 + 115406] - [2324^2]/45$$

$$= 121330.67 - 120021.69 = 1308.98$$

If you're checking, we summed the sums of blocks squared for each factor to get the three values representing the S(i)'s.

Our final tedious computation is

$$SS(total) = SUM(x^2) - (T^2)/bk$$

where the x's are the individual scores (30 of 'em, for us), so
that our Total Sum of Squares is

$$SS(total) = 183364 - 120021.69 = 63342.31$$

We're finally home. All we need is SS(error), which is

$$SS(error) = SS(total) - SS(factor) - SS(blocks)$$

$$= 63342.31 - 119.51 - 1308.98 = 61913.82$$

We'd find it worthwhile to set up the ANOVA TABLE to collect
our computations, and our thoughts:

Source	df	SS	MS	F
Factor	k - 1 = 2	119.51	59.755	$F(1) = \dfrac{59.755}{2211.208}$
Blocks	b - 1 = 14	1308.98	93.499	
Error	(k-1)(b-1)= 28	61913.82	2211.208	$F(2) = \dfrac{93.499}{2211.208}$
Total	bk - 1 = 44	63342.31	1349.598	

Thus, F(1) = .027, and F(2) = .042.

Corresponding table values are F(.1,2,28) = 2.50, so that
our computed F(1) < F(.1,2,28) and F(.1,14,28) = 1.75, and again
our computed F(2) < F(.1,14,28). In either case, we fail to reject
the implied Null Hypothesis: neither the rows nor columns--the
factors or blocks--shows a difference of the means. The blocks are
more or less as expected: the students performed in the class
(postest) as might have been expected from the pretest. The table
value for F(1) is more surprising: from previous analysis, we seem
to have indicated a difference between factors (classes). What
happened? Recall that we 'sampled' the three classes, reducing our
total sample pairs from 67 to 15. The luck of the draw might have
given us samples not representative of the population. Another
possible problem is the introduction of the blocks: the 'noise'
induced by the design might have drowned out the difference between
the factors.

If you were chairman of the department and had only this analysis to hand, you would have to conclude that, while class III
seems to have had somewhat less desirable results, the classes
performed to their potential.

Two-way Factorial Design

      Look at the data in yet one more way. I'm convinced, say,
that, on the basis of prior experience, students make a mistake
in putting off the freshman General Mathematics class for their
Sophomore, Junior, or Senior years. Further, I'm convinced that
girls are more conscientious than boys. If my suspicions are
correct, entering students should be advised most strongly that
they elect the General Mathematics class in their first two semesters. (The trouble with this advice is that, quite often, students
are not settled into a major field upon entering the university.)
Further, if I'm correct, arrangements targeted toward counselling
freshmen male students in particular ought to be given thought.
(Just what would that be?)

      Dividing the three classes of 69 students into Male and Female
and also dividing them into Freshmen and Upperclassmen, and then
sampling the four groups, seven to the sample, we have

		b		
		Freshmen	-	Upperclassmen
	Male	82 92 91 52 65 60 52		82 75 91 98 63 68 42
		T(1)=494		T(2)=519
a				
	Female	82 35 73 96 77 57 67		80 70 74 61 61 98 64
		T(3)=487		T(4)=346

      Factor A is our Male-Female partition and the computation we
need is

$$SSA = \frac{1}{14}[(494+519)^2 + (487+346)^2] - \frac{1846^2}{28}$$

where br = 14 (the number of levels of factor b times the number of
entries in each cell), the total of all four cells is 1846, and abr
=28 (the number of levels of factor a times those of b times the
number of entries in each cell). Next

$$SSB = \frac{1}{14}[(494+487)^2 + (519+346)^2] - \frac{1846^2}{28}$$

where, this time, ar = 14 (the number of levels of factor a times
the number of entries in each cell). Notice, also, that we're
adding the columns and squaring, whereas for SSA, we added the rows
and squared. Next, the INTERACTION Sums of Squares,

$$SSAB = \frac{1}{7}[494^2+519^2+487^2+346^2] - SSA - SSB - \frac{1846^2}{28}$$

where r = 7 (the number of entries in each cell. Our final lengthy
computation entails

$$SS(total) = [82^2 + 92^2 + ... + 64^2] - \frac{1846^2}{28}$$

where, obviously, we've squared each cell entry and added: 4x7=28
figures to square for this table. The Error Sums of Squares then
follows:

$$SS(error) = SS(total) - SSA - SSB - SSAB$$

and the ANOVA TABLE appears as

Source	df	SS	MS	F
A	a-1=1	1157.143	1157.143	$F(1)=\frac{MSA}{MSE}=4.377$
B	b-1=1	480.571	480.571	$F(2)=\frac{MSB}{MSE}=1.818$
AB	(a-1)(b-1)=1	984.143	984.143	$F(3)=\frac{MSAB}{MSE}=3.723$
Error	ab(r-1)=24	6345.00	264.375	
Total	abr-1=27	29667.857		

As luck would have it, all we need from the F-Ratio table
(A-7) is the figure for F(.1,1,24) = 2.93. What does our analysis
tell us? That, since F(1) > F(.1,1,24), there does indeed seem to
be reason to suppose that there is a sexual difference in response
to the General Mathematics curriculum. Do male students need more
supervision? should the syllabus be changed? Two of the three instructors in this study were female. Would the response be different if all instructors were male? female? We have room for some
analysis and corresponding adjustment, if such is called for.

Further, F(2) < F(.1,1,24), implying that freshmen and upperclassmen respond similarly to the General Mathematics syllabus.
Contrary to our gut suspicions, there seems to be no indication
that we should advise upperclassmen away from this course.

Finally, the interaction $F(3) > F(.1,1,24)$ might be explained as sexual rather than class, but bears further analysis.

Problems

1. Consider the following collection of grades:

	Freshman			Upperclassman		
	I	II	III	I	II	III
Male	97	92	85	63	78	98
	83	91	73	63	91	70
Female	94	96	76	98	73	78
	93	88	70	94	71	72

Here effort was made to select better students in the classes with notice taken of selection by sex and by class. First, arrange these student grades by class: I, II, and III (eight to each) and conduct an ANOVA test; compare with $F(.1,2,21)$.

2. Now, use the same data to conduct a two-way factorial analysis by utilizing the blocks. Conduct your tests with $F(.1,1,20)$. What conclusions seems evident? What do you think of this process of 'selecting the best' from each class? Is it preferable to random selection? Can you appreciate the instructors' dillema? Can you appreciate the statistician's reasoning?

APPLICATIONS OF THE CHI-SQUARE STATISTIC

The Chi-Square Goodness-of-Fit Test

The enrollment in the General Mathematics classes we've been following were initially as follows:

	Freshmen	Upperclassmen	
Male	33	14	47
Female	42	16	58
	75	30	105

A question arises: is this a desirable 'mix' of Freshmen and Upperclassmen? As a Freshman course, should we continue to encourage enrollment by Upperclassmen, or should advisors be told to actively discourage such enrollment?

What is a desirable 'mix'? Let's claim, first, that a desirable mix should be two-thirds Freshmen and one-third Upperclassmen. That is, of the 105 originally enrolled, our EXPECTATION is that 70 would be Freshmen and 35 Upperclassmen. Does the enrollment here reflect our Expectations or is the OBSERVED enrollment significantly different? Our test is the CHI SQUARE test, and the test statistic is

$$CHI^2 = SUM \frac{[OBSERVED - EXPECTED]^2}{EXPECTED} = SUM \frac{[O - E]^2}{E}$$

We would reject our implied Null Hypothesis: that our enrollment is an accurate reflection of our expectation, if our computed

$$CHI^2 > CHI^2(.05,1)$$

where we've set ALPHA = .05 and our Degrees of Freedom, df, equal
the number of our categories (k) less 1; that is, df = 2 - 1 = 1.

The computation becomes

$$CHI^2 = \frac{(75 - 70)^2}{70} + \frac{(30 - 35)^2}{35} = 1.07$$

The corresponding table entry for $CHI^2(.05,1)$ [Table A-6] is

$$CHI^2 = 3.84$$

Now, since our computed $CHI^2 < CHI^2(.05,1)$, we fail to reject the
Null Hypothesis, and can quit worrying obout our 'mix' of students
in General Mathematics classes.

Hold it just a minute. We show our results to the chairperson
and he/she is not pleased. It seems to me, he says, that no more
than 20 per cent of the enrollment should be Upperclassmen, else
Freshmen tend to be inhibited by their presence, fail to take part
in the class and suffer accordingly. Back to the drawing board.
This time, our EXPECTED looks like 84 Freshmen (80 per cent of the
105 enrolled) and 21 Upperclassmen (20 per cent of the 105). The
test now appears as

$$CHI^2 = \frac{(75 - 84)^2}{84} + \frac{(30 - 21)^2}{21} = 4.82$$

Against the same table value, we'd have 4.82 > 3.84, that is, our

$$CHI^2 > CHI^2(.05,1)$$

and we would reject our Null: our 'mix' is not as desired. Appropriate action, you can be sure, will be taken.

Before we upset the entire academic community by closing our
doors to Upperclassmen, let's take a more detailed look. Let's re-
classify our sample, as follows:

	Freshmen	Sophomores	Junior/Senior	
Male	33	5	9	47
Female	42	7	9	58
	75	12	18	105

Our argument goes as follows: we would 'expect' two-thirds of our
enrollment to be Freshmen and one-third Upperclassmen, with the
Sophomores making up half of the Upperclassmen. Our EXPECTATION,
then, E(Freshmen) = 70 [two-thirds of the 105 enrolled], E(Sophomores) = 17.5 (one-sixth of the 105 enrolled), and E(Junior/Senior)
= 17.5 (again, one-sixth), and our CHI^2 computed value would be
a simple extension of our previous computation:

$$CHI^2 = \frac{(75 - 70)^2}{75} + \frac{(12 - 17.5)^2}{17.5} + \frac{(18 - 17.5)^2}{17.5} = 2.076$$

Now, our categories (k) have increased to three, and our degrees of
freedom respond accordingly: our df = k - 1 = 3 - 1 = 2. So then,
our table value for CHI^2(.05,2) = 5.99, giving us additional margin to say that our computed CHI^2 < CHI^2(.05,2), and we can abide
with our Null: that our enrollments reflect the desired 'mix' we
have specified. If our department chairman grouses that we've
contrived to get by, we can respond that Sophomores are not all
so sophistocated that their presence should inhibit Freshmen. (Do
you think he'll buy that?)

We've seen here a simple extension of the CHI-SQUARE statistic
to the MULTINOMIAL situation: where we have more than two categories. The game remains the same, with one word of warning: each of
the EXPECTED values in each category should be of sufficient size.
What is 'sufficient size'? A rule of thumb says that E should be
no less than 5. In each of the categories we've been examining,
the Expected Value has been larger than 5, and so of sufficient
size. (That's a relief!)

Chi-Square Tests of Independence

You noticed, I'm sure, that the last two tables were set up
to cross-index class and sex. There is at least the possibility
of raising the question: do men or women students tend to put off

the General Mathematics course for their later school years? Are
sex and class somehow related? A cursory glance at the data does
not seem to indicate so, but let's check.

The means for doing so is to hand. All we need is the EXPEC-
TATION for each 'cell' of the table. One way to do this is to use
the data we have, and since we already have the marginal totals,
we can compute expectations as follows:

$$E(M,Fr) = \frac{47 \; 75}{105} = 33.57$$

$$E(M,So) = \frac{47 \; 12}{105} = 5.37$$

$$E(M,J/S) = \frac{47 \; 18}{105} = 8.06$$

$$E(Fe,Fr) = \frac{58 \; 75}{105} = 41.43$$

$$E(Fe,So) = \frac{58 \; 12}{105} = 6.63$$

$$E(Fe,J/S) = \frac{58 \; 18}{105} = 9.94$$

If we can rewrite our CONTINGENCY TABLE to include these expected values, it might appear as follows:

	Freshmen	Sophomores	Junior/Senior	
Male	33(33.57)	5(5.37)	9(8.06)	47
Female	42(41.43)	7(6.63)	9(9.94)	58
	75	12	18	105

Now, we proceed very much as we have done with previous CHI SQUARE tests and compare our computed CHI SQUARE value with the appropriate table entry, with df = (ROWS - 1)(COLUMNS - 1). Since we have a 2-Rows by 3-Columns Contingency Table, our df = 1x2 = 2. Our table value for ALPHA = .05, for example, would be

$$CHI^2(.05,2) = 5.99$$

The computations, then, appear as follows:

$$CHI^2 = \frac{(33 - 33.57)^2}{33.57} + \frac{(5 - 5.37)^2}{5.37} + \ldots + \frac{(9 - 9.94)^2}{9.94} = .262$$

for the six cells. Quite obviously, our computed

$$CHI^2 < CHI^2(.05,2)$$

We're not even close! The Sex and Class classifications are, as we suspected by inspection, independent.

We imposed arbitrary expectations for each cell, trying to be reasonable, but responsive to need. Suppose we were to utilize these arbitrary expectations rather than those given by the sample? We could argue that another sample of classes, either this semester or next, will produce another CHI-SQUARE value, as the composition of classes vary. Assuming equal representation of the Sexes, we allowed two-thirds of the class composition to be Freshmen; we would divide this equally between males and females, for an expectation in each Freshman cell of (1/3)105 = 35. Similarly, we allowed the remaining third to be equally divided between Sophomores and the Junior/Senior classes; dividing this once again into Male and Female, we would have each of four cells with an expectation of (1/12)105 = 8.75

Repeating the calculation immediately above, but using these imposed values for Expectations, a bit of computation yields a $CHI^2 = 3.486$, the greatest contributions coming from the Female-Freshman cell and the Male-Sophomore cell. The first because the number of female freshmen (42) exceeded the expectation (35), and the second because the number of male sophomores (5) was less than the expectation (8.75) for that cell. If we had decided on a value of $CHI^2(.1,2) = 4.605$, we still find our computed $CHI^2 < CHI^2$ from the table, but, at least, it's not embarrassing. Perhaps one or another of these cells could receive attention: why do more females than males elect the course in their freshman year? and other fascinating questions.

Problems

A travel agency must book travel and hotel accommodations well in advance, and, hence, endeavor to anticipate the desires of travelers. A recent survey (obviously contrived) sought to delve into the minds of travelers: were the desires for the coming season fairly staid? (Hawaii), somewhat adventurous? (Japan), or truly in pursuit of high adventure? (Himalayas).

The results were (can you believe?) the following:

	Hawaii	Japan	Himalayas	
Men	26	13	61	100
Women	59	29	12	100
	85	42	73	200

1. The agency, on the basis of the experience of past years, anticipates that 40 per cent of travelers will prefer Hawaii, another 40 per cent will choose Japan and other stops in the Far East, but hardly 20 per cent will book passage for a strenuous Himalayan tour. How well do these data fit the experience of past years? Do a CHI-SQUARE test on the three vacation offerings. Use ALPHA = .1. What decision seems to be open to the agency?

2. A cursory glance at the data seems to indicate a decided discrepancy between the desires of Men and those of Women. Is this illusory or real? Do a CHI-SQUARE test on the cells. Use the data to compute the Expected values. Again, test using ALPHA = .1. (What degrees of freedom?) Again, what decision seems to be open to the agency? If the result of the test is significant, what addition questions would seem reasonable?

14

SIMPLE LINEAR
REGRESSION

Bivariate Data and Correlation

We took a look at this approach to data analysis back in Chapter 4. We want to repeat and extend this approach -- and try to exhibit some of its use and power -- and some of the limitations we can't ignore.

For example, for our beloved General Mathematics students, is the ACT score (or the SAT, if that's available) a valid predictor of success in the course? Should we, as some schools and states are doing, limit opportunity? should we prohibit the student with an ACT score, for example, below 12 from enrolling in the class -- the argument being that his/her prospects for success are dim to none? [In defense of schools, we should say that some of this arbitrary rule-making is economic rather than scholarly.]

Here are 49 pairs of scores for our General Mathematics group: the first score is the student's ACT score in Mathematics (on a scale of 0 to 36), the second his/her score on the Final exam in the course. [Recall that we started with some 105 students and now we're finishing with 49! It's not quite that bad: not all students had an ACT score available.]

(23,82)	(26,93)	(17,91)	(10,80)	(15,82)	(12,63)	(22,82)
(16,78)	(14,82)	(11,73)	(21,83)	(13,70)	(15,80)	(16,74)
(21,82)	(19,85)	(16,73)	(11,61)	(9,71)	(17,92)	(7,75)
(6,73)	(5,48)	(21,91)	(16,82)	(8,50)	(14,52)	(21,88)
(24,91)	(6,61)	(17,75)	(10,71)	(13,65)	(18,75)	(14,77)
(18,55)	(14,60)	(12,52)	(11,70)	(1,54)	(14,42)	(17,59)
(19,65)	(16,73)	(8,55)	(19,72)	(9,67)	(6,61)	(15,52)

Once again, what does anyone do with such a mass of data?
A glance tells us that students with low ACT scores TEND to score
low once again on the Final, but not consistently. Look just at
the last row: one student with an ACT of 19 (respectable if not
magnificent) scored 65 on the Final; another with an ACT of 9 did
even better, a 67 on the Final. The difficulty with this sort of
analysis is that looking at the trees, we lose sight of the forest:
no one can set policy this way.

Let's do as we did in Chapter 4: a Scatter Diagram.

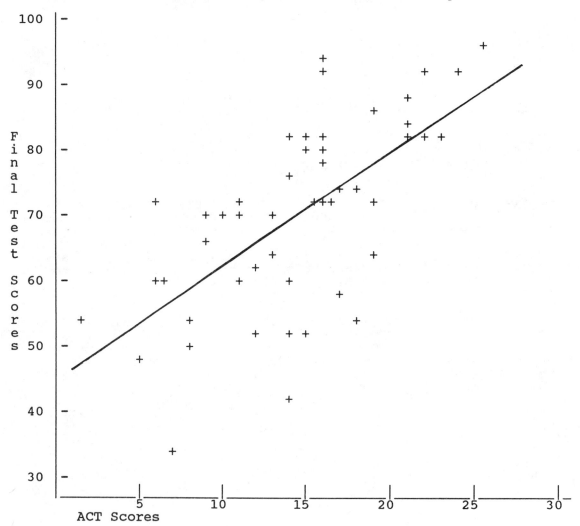

The Scatter Diagram helps, and, back to Chapter 4, the numerical value for the COEFFICIENT OF CORRELATION, r, will give us additional insight.

$$r = \frac{SUM(x - \bar{x})(y - \bar{y})}{SQRT[SUM(x - \bar{x})\wedge2] \ SQRT[SUM(y - \bar{y})\wedge2]}$$

The Correlation Coefficient for our 49 pairs is r = .6578. All values of r lie between -1 and 1. A positive value indicates a positive correlation (what else?). The closer to 1, the stronger the correlation: if r = 1, all pairs would lie along a straight line with positive slope (rising from left to right, assuming the scales are as we have them--increasing from left to right and bottom to top). A negative value would indicate that an increase in one set of values, say the horizontal, would be accompanied with a decrease in the other.

Incidentally, in the notation of Chapter 12, we can abbreviate our formula to read:

$$r = \frac{SS(XY)}{SQRT[SS(X)] \ SQRT[SS(Y)]}$$

While we're at it, there's another statistical measure you'll find on your calculator, the COVARIANCE, given by

$$Cov(X,Y) = \frac{1}{n - 1}SUM(x - \bar{x})(y - \bar{y}) = \frac{1}{n - 1}SS(XY)$$

which, again, measures the strength of the relationship between your two sets of data. The Covariance for our 49 pairs of figures is Cov(ACT,Final) = 50.095. The Covariance is, unlike the Correlation Coefficient, not limited to values between -1 and 1. The size of the Covariance value is interpretable only in comparison to some other corresponding pairs and their Covariance figure.

What do we know? Or, to address our initial question, can we (should we) use the ACT scores to predict Final test scores--or, as we indicated is done, to limit enrollment in General Mathematics courses? Neither the Scatter Diagram nor the Correlation value, r, seems to give us much confidence. If you're willing to fail those with Final grades below 60, you'll find, even with this small group several you would have disallowed passing, and several you would have allowed in failing. The value, r = .6578, tells us that the predictive value of the ACT is not perfect.

The Least Squares Line

There is one more thing we can do to help us interpret the pairs in the Scatter diagram: fit a line to the data that minimizes the squares of the distances of the points in the diagram to the line. Some of the points will lie above the line--the measure of the distance to such will be positive, others will lie below the line--the measure of the distances to such will take on the opposite sign, negative. To get the line that fits best, the positive and negative distance values should wipe each other out. The LEAST SQUARES LINE is designed to do just that. The line we want is

$$y = b(0) + b(1)x$$

where $b(1) = SS(XY)/SS(X)$ and $b(0) = \bar{y} - b(1)\bar{x}$. Again, resorting to our calculator, the coefficients we want give us the line

$$y = 45.6 + 1.705x$$

which is the line we've imposed on the data in the Scatter Diagram. The strength of the correlation among the data points lies not in the slope of the line nor in its y-intercept, but in the 'spread'-- how close to the line are the points in the diagram? You'll note here an almost spooky repetition of the diagram in Chapter 4: the values to the upper right are close to the line, those to the lower left are well scattered. In the Scatter diagram for Chapter 4, we were correlating ACT with Pretest scores; here, we're correlating ACT with Postest scores. We've lost voices along the way, but the melody lingers on: people continue to behave consistently, and, consistently, we are better able to predict high-scorers than we are low-scorers. One last time: would you use ACT scores to bar the doors to low-scoring students?

How good is our Least Squares line? There is a measure of goodness in a value, the ERROR SUMS OF SQUARES, given by

$$SSE = SUM(d)^2 = SUM(y - y)^2 = SS(Y) - \frac{SS(XY)^2}{SS(X)}$$

which sums the squares of the distances from the Least Squares to each and every one of the 49 points. Now,

$$SS(Y) = SUM(Y)^2 - [SUM(Y)]^2/n = 256502 - (3448)^2/49 = 13875.388$$

$$SS(X) = SUM(X)^2 - [SUM(X)]^2/n = 11669 - (709)^2/49 = 1410.204$$

$$SS(XY) = SUM(XY) - SUM(X)SUM(Y)/n = 52295 - (709)(3448)/49 = 2404.5$$

so that SSE = 13875.388 - (2404.551)^2/1410.204 = 9775.367

Not exactly zero. But, you better believe it, no other line
will give us a smaller SSE. [Why do you think we call it LEAST...]

The Simple Linear Regression Model

With the machinery we've set up, we can (within limits we'll
define) set up a predictor equation that relates our ACT scores to
our Final Test scores. Our equation is our least squares line with
an additional value to allow for error (not all the points lie just
on the least squares line, do they?). For our sample the equation
looks like

$$y = b(0) + b(1)x + e$$

where b(0) is the intercept value (for our data, b(0) = 45.6) and
b(1) is the slope (b(1) = 1.705). What can we say about e, the
error term? We can compute the ERROR VARIANCE, namely,

$$s^2 = \frac{SSE}{n-2}$$

Our SSE = 9775.367, just above. Our n = 49. So s^2 = 207.9865
and the standard deviation for the error, s = 14.42.

What is our claim, then? That, for a chosen value of x, say
x = 18, the corresponding value for y will be

$$y = 45.6 + 1.705(18) = 76.29$$

What about a larger collection of pairs of scores? If we were to
collect thousands (from where?), and choose only those with ACT
scores of 18, we would find the corresponding Final Test scores
to be 76.29. Exactly? Hardly. The error term tells us that
we will find the Final Test scores for ACT's of 18 centering at
76.29 and that most of them (68 per cent, by the Empirical Rule)
in the range between 76.29 +/- 14.42 or in the interval

$$(61.87, 90.71)$$

Try any other ACT score: let x = 20, plug and chug. The same error
standard deviation serves.

Which brings us to our assumptions.

(i) For a given value of x, the corresponding
y-values will center on the least-squares
line.

(ii) For each given value of x, the error in the
corresponding y-values are normally distributed.

(iii) The variance for these errors (and, of course,
the standard deviation) is the same, no matter
which x-value you choose. There's a name for
this: HOMOSCEDASTICITY. Try that in general
conversation. [If the variance for these
errors were NOT the same, we'd have HETERO-
SCEDASTICITY, naturally.]

(iv) The errors for each y are independent of each
other.

The sample is a reflection, or is presumed to be a reflection,
of the population. Correspondingly, then, there is a linear regression model for the population, with BETAS replacing the b's
and SIGMA for s.

Does a linear relationship exist?

We looked at a Scatter Diagram of the ACT-Final pairs and
noted, didn't we?, that there seems to be tendency for students
with low ACT's to score low on the Final, and vice versa. The
tendency isn't very strong. Our Correlation Coefficient of

$$r = .6578$$

indicated a positive, not overwhelming, relationship. Further,
our Error Standard Deviation of

$$s = 14.42$$

verified our suspicions: you would have a trouble predicting a
student's Final score from his ACT score. An ACT score of 18 might
give him a final course grade of anything from D to A! And that's
only for some two-thirds of the scores. Could such a student, let's
don't say the word, fail? Of course he could.

There's even more trouble in this model. Someone can always
take pairs of values, plug them into formulas, and get a linear
model. If he had failed to avail himself of a Scatter Diagram, he
might never realize the data would be better served by another --

a CURVILINEAR model. A polynomial, an exponential, or a logarith-
mic curve might be a much better predictor. How would he know?
One obvious way: look at the Scatter Diagram. Another is to test:
the hypotheses are

$$H(o): BETA(1) = 0 \text{ (Slope is zero; x tells us nothing about y)}$$

$$H(a): BETA(1) =/ 0$$

The test statistic is

$$t = \frac{b(1) - BETA(1)}{s/SQRT[SS(X)]}$$

with n - 2 df. Since our null hypothesis is that BETA(1) = 0, our
computations appear as

$$t = \frac{1.7051}{14.42/SQRT(1410.204)} = 4.44$$

Tested against t(.05,47) = 1.68, our computed t > t(.05,47) and we
do indeed reject the Null in favor of the Alternative hypothesis.
The slope is NOT zero. But, as we've argued (we're not trying to
be testy, just cautious), the predictive abilities of the ACT score
is not too reliable. Further, this test DOESN'T say that a linear
relationship must hold; it only says that, if you were to endeavor
to find the Least Squares line, its slope would not be zero. Another sort of relationship, curvilinear, might very well be better.
Again, don't fail to do the simple-minded thing: look at the diagram.

A 90% Confidence Interval for the slope, BETA(1), follows the
same computations:

$$b(1) - t(.05,47)s[b(1)] < BETA(1) < b(1) + t(.05,47)s[b(1)]$$

$$1.7051-(1.68)[.384] < BETA(1) < 1.7051+(1.68)[.384]$$

$$1.06 < BETA(1) < 2.35$$

where .384 = 14.42/SQRT(1410.204).

Once again, we're assured that a relationship does indeed
exist between the ACT scores and the Final test scores (did we
doubt it?), but don't let the numbers lead you. Take a good
look at the diagram... you know the game.

A second test, with the same hypotheses, is a measure of the STRENGTH OF THE MODEL. The test statistic is

$$t = \frac{r}{SQRT[\frac{1 - r^2}{n - 2}]}$$

Since, the correlation coefficient, r, has been available all this time, let's use it: for r = .6578,

$$t = \frac{.6578}{SQRT[\frac{.5673}{47}]} = \frac{.6578}{.10986} = 5.987$$

Tested against t(.1,47) = 1.68, obviously, our computed t>t(.1,47) by a considerable margin and we're assured that the linear model fits the data quite well.

The value, r^2, we used in the t-Test above for STRENGTH OF MODEL has a name of its own:

r^2 = the COEFFICIENT OF DETERMINATION

For our data, r^2 = (.6573)^2 = .432 and, since |r| < 1

0 < r^2 < 1

The Coefficient of Determination might be computed directly:

$$r^2 = 1 - \frac{SSE}{SS(Y)}$$

Estimation of Prediction

One last time (almost), we want to examine the Least Squares Line and its predictive value: for a given x = x(o) (the ACT score we are given at the beginning of the semester's work), how much confidence can we place on the corresponding y-value (the Final Test score) it predicts? For example, for x = 18, the predicted value of y = 76.29 [in the language, this is MU(y|x(o))]. For a given ACT - for ACT = 18 - what range of Final Test scores might we expect, with, say, a 90 per cent Confidence? Our interval appears as

$$y - t(.05,47)(s)SQRT[\frac{1}{n} + \frac{[x(o) - \bar{x}]^2}{SS(X)}]$$

$$< MU[y|x(o)] < y + t(.05,47)(s)SQRT[\frac{1}{n} + \frac{[x(o) - \bar{x}]^2}{SS(X)}]$$

$$76.29 - 1.68(.384)SQRT[\frac{1}{49} + \frac{(18 - 14.47)^2}{1410.204}]$$

$$< MU[y|18] < 76.29 + 1.68(.384)SQRT[\frac{1}{49} + \frac{(18 - 14.47)^2}{1410.204}]$$

$$76.18 < MU[y|80] < 76.40$$

which gives us considerable confidence in our model.

One last question of the same sort: for a given value of x, say x = 18, what will the next corresponding value of y be? We may be seeming to split hairs here, but there is a semantic difference. Above, we were looking for a range of values of y to cover 90 per cent of the scores we might run across (with x = 18). Now, we're trying to predict a particular y. As you might imagine, not much changes, but the interval is extending somewhat by a small change in the multiplier to:

$$SQRT[1 + \frac{1}{n} + \frac{[x(o) - \bar{x}]^2}{SS(X)}]$$

the value of which is approximately 1.01, so that the interval now appears as

$$76.29 - 1.68(.384)(1.01) < y(x = 18) < 76.29 + 1.68(.384)(1.01)$$

$$76.29 - .6545 < y(x = 18) < 76.29 + .6545$$

$$75.6355 < y(x = 18) < 76.9445$$

Hardly half a point difference. Have you ever lost an A by half a point?

Problems

A random selection of pairs of values from our General Mathematics classes gives us the following:

        (26,93)   (23,82)   (5,48)   (16,73)   (7,35)
        (21,88)   (10,71)   (11,73)   (14,77)   (14,52)

1. Construct a Scatter Diagram of the data and examine: do the data exhibit a linear or nonlinear relationship?

2. Find the Correlation Coefficient, r.

3. Find the Covariance, Cov(X,Y).

4. Find the Least Squares Line. To do so, find $\bar{x}$ and $\bar{y}$, SS(X), SS(Y), and SS(XY). Then find intercept, b(o), and slope, b(1).

5. Find SSE, the Error Sums of Squares.

6. Find the Error Variance and Standard Deviation.

7. Test for Linearity: let H(o): BETA(1) = 0, and H(a): BETA(1) =/ 0. Test against t(ALPHA/2,df) = t(.05/df). Do we support H(o)?

8. Find a 90% C.I. for the slope, BETA(1)

9. Find the Strength of the Model. Test against t(.1,df). What conclusion do you draw?

10. Find the Coefficient of Determination, first from your value of the Correlation Coefficient and again directly.

11. Find a 90% C.I. for MU[y|x = 15].

12. Predict y for x = 15 with 90% Confidence.

MULTIPLE LINEAR REGRESSION

Using More than One Predictor Variable

In Chapter 14 we used the ACT scores for our General Mathematics students to 'predict' their Final Test scores. If you look back, you'll find SSE = 9775.367, which tells us, among other information, that the ACT is not a full explanation of student performance. If we want to gain a fuller understanding of the student, we need more data. It just so happens (!) that we have the information we need: Each student, with one exception, took a Pretest which, if you'll recall, was a measure of the student's arithmetic skills. Suppose we were to use BOTH of these measures? That is, suppose we were to use the ACT score AND the Arithmetic Skills Test score to predict the Final Test score. Would we improve our predictive abilities to any measure? Let's see.

The triples, (ACT, AST, Postest), for 48 students appear as follows:

```
(23,29,82) (26,26,93) (17,24,91) (10,22,80) (15,25,82) (12,23,63)
(22,21,82) (16,21,78) (14,23,82) (11,23,73) (21,22,83) (13,23,70)
(15,22,80) (16,23,74) (21,24,82) (19,27,85) (16,23,73) (11,21,61)
( 9,30,71) (17,29,92) ( 7,26,75) ( 6,25,73) ( 5,21,48) (21,30,91)
(16,26,82) ( 8,22,50) (14,23,52) (21,22,88) (24,27,91) ( 6,22,61)
(17,27,75) (10,21,71) (13,24,65) (18,24,75) (14,28,77) (18,25,55)
(14,22,60) (12,25,52) (11,21,70) (14,26,42) (17,21,59) (19,27,65)
(16,25,73) ( 8,22,55) (19,24,72) ( 9,24,67) ( 6,26,61) (15,22,52)
```

With the immeasurable assistance of a MINITAB computer package we were handed the following regression equation:

$$\text{Postest} = 28.4 + 1.32\text{ACT} + 0.989\text{AST}$$

This model tells us, for example, that a student with an ACT score of 23 (out of a possible 36) and an AST score of 29 (out of a possible 30) should score

$$28.4 + 1.32(23) + 0.989(29) = 87.141$$

on the Postest. Did he? The first triple is (23,29,82). So he scored 82 on the Postest. The model is off a bit:

$$82 - 87.141 = -5.141$$

But we're not to expect a perfect fit. We're claiming here, as we did in Chapter 14, that the Error Sums of Squares in this model is less than that for any other. In Chapter 14, we drew a Least Squares line through a Scatter Diagram of the data that expressed our thoughts geometrically. Here, since we have a triple for each student, our line becomes a SURFACE. For this first student, the value, 87.141, lies on the surface, and the actual score, 82, lies just below; 5.141 units just below, to be precise.

What happens if we use three predictors instead of two? We simply extend our model: for each data point, we have a '4-tuple' and tell our package we want to REGRESS the values in columns 2, 3, and 4 on the values in column 1. The package does its thing and gives us the corresponding REGRESSION EQUATION.

Common sense tells us that we know a bit more about each student than we knew in Chapter 14: we have two predictors in place of one. How much good have we done? Well, the print-out of the computer package tells us that our SSE = 5044.9: we've accounted for about half the error (the value in Chapter 14 was SSE = 9775.4) There's one little quibble: we dropped a data point (the AST was not available for one student), so that these two values are not strictly comparable, but the difference is quite small.

Test for Significance

The ANOVA table gives us the information to test the relationship between the PREDICTORS and the FINAL TEST score. The ratio of the Mean Squares values for Regression and Error gives us a measure of the strength of this relationship. The test goes like this:

H(o): BETA = 0 for all predictors-none influences the FINAL score

H(a): at least one of the BETA's is not zero

The test statistic is the F-ratio:

$$F = \frac{\text{Regression Mean Square}}{\text{Error Mean Square}}$$

with k and n - k - 1 degrees of freedom, for k, the number of predictors (two for us), and n, the number of data entries (48 for us)
If we test at ALPHA = .1, the table (Table A-7) entry is

$$F(.1,2,45) = 2.43$$

From the ANOVA table, F = 1452.4/112.1 = 12.9563. Since the computed F > F(.1,2,45), we conclude that at least one of the scores,
the ACT score and/or the AST score, is a valid predictor of the
Final Test score.

But which? After giving us the Regression Equation, the
computer print-out gives us the following table:

Predictor	Coef	Stdev	t-ratio
Constant	28.40	14.75	1.93
C2 (our ACT score)	1.3200	0.3118	4.23
C3 (our AST score)	0.9891	0.6312	1.57

where the t-ratio values are computed as t = Coef/Stdev. If we
test these against t(.1,45) = 1.301, we find that both of the
t-ratio values from the table are larger: 4.23 > 1.301 and 1.57 >
1.301, giving us some assurance that BOTH of these scores exert
influence on the Final Score, the ACT score perhaps demonstrating
a more significant predictive ability than the AST score.

The first line of the table implies that there is still a good
deal to be explained: there are significant factors [since the t-
value of 1.93 is also greater than t(.1,45)] that might assist us
in predicting the Final Test score. If the students' high school
mathematics scores are available, we might introduce this as a
third factor; we might shuffle factors: give up the AST score for
another that makes a more significant contribution. Let's not just
introduce another test on top of the ACT and AST: keep in mind the
limits of human exasperation.

Once again, because 'it's there' for the taking, we can give
ourselves additional insight by establishing CONFIDENCE INTERVALS
for the coefficient values:

$$b(i)-t(ALPHA/2,n-k-1)s(b(i))<BETA(i)<b(i)-t(ALPHA/2,n-k-1)s(b(i))$$

For the ACT score, the Confidence Interval for the coefficient is:
(with t(ALPHA/2,n-k-1) = t(.05,45) = 1.68)

$$1.32 - 1.68(.3118) < \text{BETA(ACT)} < 1.32 + 1.68(.3118)$$

$$.796 < \text{BETA(ACT)} < 1.844$$

and for the AST (the Arithmetic Skills Test), the Confidence Interval for the coefficient is:

$$.9891 - 1.68(.6312) < \text{BETA(AST)} < .9891 + 1.68(.6312)$$

$$-.071 < \text{BETA(AST)} < 2.050$$

This last again gives us pause: it's entirely within the realm of the possible that this coefficient is zero. It's decision time! Do we abandon the test? [Protest! If the student can't add fractions...] Do we revise the test, perhaps testing more than simple arithmetic skills? Do we sample again? Worries!

A valid set of predictors

Any regression model can be attacked as perhaps inadequate for the purpose intended. There isn't an investigator alive who hasn't echoed Sherlock Holmes' cry, More data! But all good things must finally come to decision. Some assurance that the model has predictive ability is obtained by using the COEFFICIENT OF DETERMINATION,

$$R^2 = 1 - \frac{SSE}{SST}$$

For our model, $R^2 = 1 - \frac{5044.9}{7949.7} = 1 - .6346 = .3654.$ Now, we would

dearly love to have $R^2 = 1$, but life's not like that. The test for the adequacy of our Coefficient of Determination is the following:

$$F = \frac{\dfrac{R^2}{k}}{\dfrac{1 - R^2}{n - k - 1}}$$

With $R^2 = .3654$, $n = 48$, $k = 2$, our $F = 12.955$, just the value we obtained off the ANOVA table (with a bit of round-off error) from the computer printout. Now, since our computed $F > F(.1,2,45)$, we are assured, once again, that our model, for all its apparent inadequacies, has some predictive ability. We do not have to throw the baby out with the bath water. (Rinse him off?)

But what about the nagging doubt concerning the Arithmetic Skills Test? Can we do without it? Administration of the test is exasperating: not all students show up; makeup tests have to be devised and administered; students fail to pass the test and 'help sessions' have to be scheduled and taught so that instructors and students are assured that each and everyone has had opportunity.

One way to find out is to put the PAIRS of data, (ACT,Final), into the computer and get a regression equation--along with the other information--on just this predictor, without the AST factor to cloud the issue. The computer gives us the following:

C1(our Final Test score) = 50.2 + 1.46C2(our ACT score)

Predictor	Coef	Stdev	t-ratio
Constant	50.181	4.691	10.70
C2 (ACT scores)	1.4606	0.3029	4.82

$s = 10.69$ $R^2 = 33.6\%$ $R^2(adj) = 32.1\%$

ANOVA

Source	df	SS	MS
Regression	1	2656.4	2656.4
Error	46	5255.5	114.3
Total	47	7911.9	

The Coefficient of Determination for this REDUCED model, then, is the following:

$$R^2 = 1 - \frac{SSE}{SST} = 1 - \frac{5255.5}{7911.9} = 1 - .664 = .336$$

Let's label the first Coefficient of Determination, for the model including both predictive factors (ACT and AST) as R(c), and the the one we just figured for the single predictive factor (ACT) as R(r), and perform the following test:

$$F = \frac{[R(c)^2 - R(r)^2]/NU(1)}{[1 - R(c)^2]/NU(2)}$$

where NU(1) = 2 (the number of predictors), and NU(2) = 45, for n - k - 1. (n = the number of data points and k = the number of predictors).

A bit of arithmetic gives is F = 1.053. The corresponding table value is F(.1,2,45) = 2.43. This time our computed

$$F < F(.1,2,45)$$

which tells us, to our chagrin, that the loss of the AST, the Arithmetic Skills Test, was significant. We'll have a better regression model with both predictors than we have with just the one.

The F-ratio obtained from the quotient, MSR/MST, or from

$$F = \frac{R^2/1}{\dfrac{1 - R^2}{46}}$$

gives us F = 23.24 (from MSR/MSE) and F = 23.28 from the expression using the Correlation Coefficient; the difference is due to round-off. The corresponding table value for F(.1,1,46) = 2.83, sending a message, loud and clear, that the AST score surely is a factor in the regression model.

Another useful bit of information is the following, from the MINITAB package:

CORRELATION

	Final	ACT
ACT	0.579	
AST	0.339	0.272

We are particularly interested in the last figure: the correlation between the AST and ACT scores is given as 0.272. We would have found it undesirable to have a large value here; some correlation is inevitable: we're testing the same individual. Fortunately, the figure is not unreasonable. The effect we're endeavoring to control is one called MULTICOLLINEARITY, which can adversely affect our regression model. Fortunately for the sake of our argument, the two tests examine different aspects of the individual's knowledge and the interaction is small. Once again, the correlation between the ACT and the Final Test score is greater than the correlation between the Arithmetic Skills Test and the Final Test score, corroborating our previous suspicions and analysis.

Problems

Let's consider a random sample of the data we've been examining:
the triples, (FINAL, ACT, AST), for ten of our students are the
following:

$$(32,21,22)$$
$$(52,12,25)$$
$$(73, 6,25)$$
$$(77,14,28)$$
$$(88,21,22)$$
$$(75,18,24)$$
$$(85,19,27)$$
$$(82,23,29)$$
$$(71,10,21)$$
$$(70,13,23)$$

1. Find the Regression Equation

2. Use F(.1,k,n-k-1) to test the Null Hypothesis: all BETA's = 0,
       against the Alternative Hypothesis: not all BETA's = 0,
       where the BETA's are the regression coefficients.

3. Use t(.1,n-k-1) to test the individual predictors.

4. Find Confidence Intervals for the BETA's with t(.05,n-k-1)

5. Find the Coefficient of Determination and test for adequacy.

Consider the same ten students we've chosen and append their final
letter grades: a 4 corresponds to A, 3 to B, 2 to C, 1 to D, and 0
to F.

$$(3,83,21,22)$$
$$(0,52,12,25)$$
$$(2,73, 6,25)$$
$$(2,77,14,28)$$
$$(3,88,21,22)$$
$$(2,75,18,24)$$
$$(3,85,19,27)$$
$$(3,82,23,29)$$
$$(2,71,10,21)$$
$$(2,70,13,23)$$

6. Find the regression equation (regressing Columns 2, 3, and 4 on
       column 1 and analyze as above. [Our sample contains no A's,
       but I assure you there were a representative collection of
       them!]

Chapter 2

1. a] Noting that the lowest value is 0.2 and the highest, 9.8,
   suggests $\dfrac{H - L}{K} = \dfrac{9.8 - 0.2}{5} = \dfrac{9.6}{5} = 1.92$, or a class width
   of 2.0. Tabulating:

0.0-1.9	2.0-3.9	4.0-5.9	6.0-7.9	8.0-9.9
1.2	3.7	5.3	7.3	8.0
0.7	3.7	4.5	6.5	8.8
1.1	3.5	4.5	6.5	8.4
0.2	3.8	5.0	6.0	8.0
	2.5	4.2	6.7	8.1
	3.1	5.7	6.9	9.4
	2.8	5.5	6.4	8.9
	3.9	5.7	6.9	9.8
	2.0		7.4	9.8
	3.8		6.9	
	2.7		7.2	
	2.5		6.1	
	3.7			
	2.3			
	3.0			
	3.6			
	3.9			

The histogram then appears as:

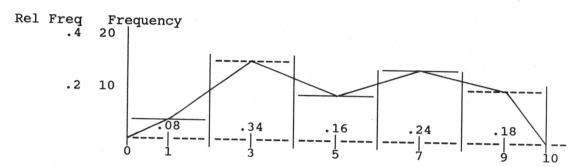

The graph contains more than the desired histogram. We'll
refer to this graph for succeeding problems.

1. b] Our formula, $\dfrac{H - L}{K} = \dfrac{9.8 - 0.2}{10} = \dfrac{9.6}{10} = .96$, which suggests a

class width of 1.0. Tabulating, we have the following:

0	1	2	3	4	5	6	7	8	9
0.7	1.2	2.5	3.7	4.8	5.3	6.5	7.3	8.0	9.4
0.2	1.1	2.8	3.7	4.5	5.0	6.5	7.4	8.8	9.8
		2.0	3.5	4.2	5.7	6.0	7.2	8.4	9.8
		2.7	3.8		5.5	6.7		8.0	
		2.5	3.1		5.7	6.9		8.7	
		2.3	3.9			6.4		8.9	
			3.8			6.9			
			3.7			6.9			
			3.0			6.1			
			3.9						

And now the corresponding histogram:

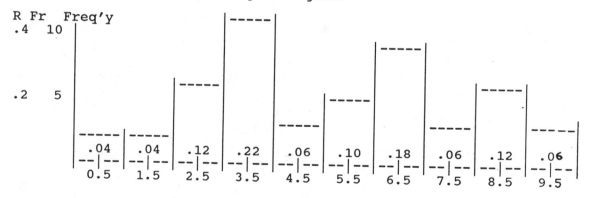

2. The analysis remains as in Problem #1. Only the vertical scale
   changes. The vertical scale for relative frequency is indicated
   above [#1a] and, for convenience, the boxes contain the parts
   per hundred.

3. The illustration [#1a] has the frequency polygon superimposed.
   Ordinarily, the polygon would stand alone.

4.

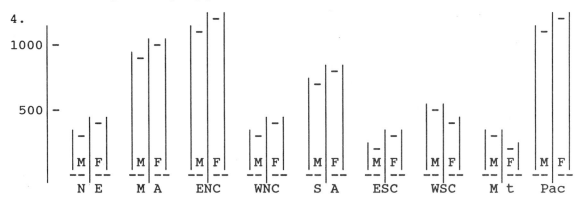

Note that female enrollment is higher than male enrollment in
most regions. If your concern is equal opportunity for females
in higher education, which regions would elicit your concern?
The bar graph, as sketched, may raise questions, but yield only
only partial answers. Consider the West South Central (WSC) region: two states show lower female enrollment, Oklahoma and
Texas. Can you suggest why this might be? Before you mount
your white charger and ride off yelling chauvanism, at least
check enrollment against population proportions. Your task,
as a statistician, is not merely to suggest but to investigate.

5.

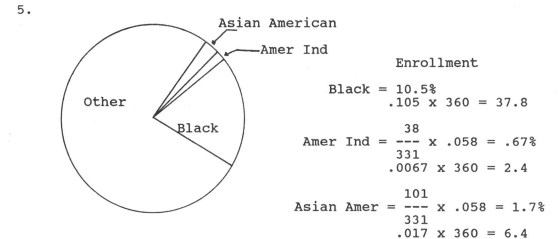

Enrollment

Black = 10.5%
.105 x 360 = 37.8

$$\text{Amer Ind} = \frac{38}{331} \times .058 = .67\%$$
.0067 x 360 = 2.4

$$\text{Asian Amer} = \frac{101}{331} \times .058 = 1.7\%$$
.017 x 360 = 6.4

We note that just over one-eighth of the enrollment falls into
these categories. Does this enrollment reflect the population?
Is any group UNDERrepresented? OVERrepresented? Why? Again,
your task is not merely to conjecture, but to demonstrate that
your conjecture has substance (or lacks substance).

Chapter 3

1. a) Taken in the order given:

```
2 | 8,2,8,9
3 | 4,2,5
4 | 9,6
5 | 8,6,2
6 | 9,1
7 | 6,9,0,7
```

With leaves ordered from smallest to largest:

```
2 | 2,8,8,9
3 | 2,4,5
4 | 6,9
5 | 2,6,8
6 | 1,9
7 | 0,6,7,9
```

b) Mean, $\bar{x}$ = 49.94; Median, Md = $\dfrac{49 + 52}{2}$ = 50.5; Midrange, Mr = $\dfrac{79 + 22}{2}$ = 50.5; Mode (none).

c) Range, r = 79 - 22 = 57; Mean Absolute Deviation, MAD = $\dfrac{296.9}{18}$ = 16.49; Variance, s^2 = 372.879; Standard deviation, s = 19.31; Coefficient of Variation, CV = $\dfrac{19.31}{49.94}$ 100 = 38.66

d) Fiftieth percentile score = median = 18 $\dfrac{50}{100}$ = 9th score exactly, so we average the 9th and 10th scores: $\dfrac{49 + 52}{2}$ = 50.5; 25th percentile score = 18 $\dfrac{25}{100}$ = 4.5 - or 5th score: 32; 75th percentile score = 18 $\dfrac{75}{100}$ = 13.5 - or 14th score: 69.

The box-&-whisker plot:

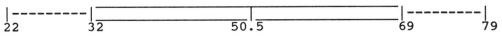

```
|---------|========T=====================|---------|
22        32       50.5                  69        79
```

e)   (i) $+/-1 = \dfrac{x(i) - \bar{x}}{s} = \dfrac{x(i) - 49.94}{19.31}$, $x(i) = 49.94 +/- 19.31$

or an interval: (30.63, 69.25); ten of 18 scores, or 56%

(ii) $+/-2 = \dfrac{x(i) - 49.94}{19.31}$, $x(i) = 49.94 +/- 2(19.31) =$

49.94 +/- 38.62, or an interval: (11.32, 88.56); all
18 scores or 100%

(iii) $z = \dfrac{70 - 49.94}{19.31} = 1.04$ (iv) $z = \dfrac{29 - 49.94}{19.31} = -1.08$

(Note that these scores, in (iii) and (iv), are a bit
above and below one standard deviation of the mean.)

f)   (i) From part e (ii), scores in the interval, (11.32, 88.56)
are within two standard deviations of the mean. All 18
scores--or 100% of the scores--are included.

(ii) Again, the obvious answer is yes. The Chebyshev measure
is not very 'fine.'

g) See part e (i) and (ii). The Empirical Rule (by means of
which we judge whether the frequency polygon--or stem & leaf
plot-- is bell-shaped) is only partially satisfied. We need
more data before we assert that we have a normally distributed set.

2. a)   0 | 3,1,4
         0 | 9,7,6,5,9,8,6,5,8,8,9,6
         1 | 2,0,2,4,4,1,3,0,1,4,3,0,3,4,4,2,2,1,4,4
         1 | 7,5,6,5,6,9,6,7,6,7,8,8,7,7,7,9,6,9,5
         2 | 3,2,1,4,1,1,1,4
         2 | 6

(Note that we've split our stems: values 0 thru 4 and 5
thru 9, for example, have separate 0 stems.)

b) $\bar{x} = 13.73$, Md = 14   (There are 63 scores; the middle score is
the 32nd score; for convenience, we've ordered the 3rd row of
the stem & leaf plot:

   1 | 0,0,0,1,1,1,2,2,2,2,3,3,3,4,4,4,[4],4,4,4

$Mr = \dfrac{26 - 1}{2} = 12.5$; Mode = 14.

c) Range = 26 - 1 = 25

   Mean Absolute Deviation = $\dfrac{277.11}{63}$ = 4.4

   Variance, s^2 = 31.2; Standard deviation, s = 5.58

   Coefficient of variation, CV = $\dfrac{5.58}{13.73}$ 100 = 40.

d) (i) Fiftieth percentile score = median = 63 $\dfrac{50}{100}$ = 31.5;

       32nd score is 14.

    (ii) First quartile score (25th percentile) = 63 $\dfrac{25}{100}$ = 15.75;

       16th score is 10.

       Third quartile score (75th percentile) = 63 $\dfrac{75}{100}$ = 47.25;

       48th score is 17.

   (iii) Box & whisker plot:

e) (i) +/-1 = $\dfrac{x(i) - 13.73}{5.58}$, x(i) = 13.73 +/- 5.58; the interval

       is (8.15, 19.31). Forty-two scores lie within one stan-
       dard deviation of the mean--or 67%

    (ii) +/-2 = $\dfrac{x(i) - 13.73}{5.58}$, x(i) = 13.73 +/- 2(5.58); the inter

       val is (2.57, 24.89). Sixty-one scores lie within two
       standard deviations of the mean--or 97%

   (iii) z(1) = -2.281; z(3) = -1.923; z(8) = -1.027; z(9)= .848;
       z(19) = .944; z(21) = 1.303; z(24) = 1.84; z(26) = 2.199

f) (i) See part e(ii)

    (ii) +/-3 = $\dfrac{x(i) - 13.73}{5.58}$, x(i) = 13.73 +/- 3(5.58); the inter

val is (-3.01, 30.47). All scores lie within three stan
dard deviations of the mean.

g) From parts e (i) and (ii), 67% of all scores lie within one
one standard deviation of the mean, while 97% lie within two
--quite 'close' to the specifications of the Empirical Rule.

3. If we encode, $\bar{x}$ = 48.125, $10\bar{x}$ = 481.25, and $10\bar{x}$ + 2000 = 2481.25

Standard deviation, s = 13.822, and Variance, s^2 = 191.05

4. Mean:
$$\frac{(23.08)(25) + 100}{26} = 26.038 \text{ for an increase of about 2.96}$$

Median: Average the 13th and 14th scores: $\dfrac{23 + 23}{2}$ = 23, for no
change.

Midrange: $\dfrac{100 - 6}{2}$ = 47, for an increase of 24.

Mode: There was none before and none now.

In general, as here, the median is usually least affected by
outliers.

Range: 100 - 6 = 94, for an increase of 50.

Mean Absolute Deviation, MAD = $\dfrac{216.24 + (100 - 23.08)}{26}$ = 11.2754
for an increase of 2.625

Variance, s^2 = 356.118, and Standard deviation, s = 18.871

Coefficient of variation, CV = $\dfrac{18.871}{26.038}$ 100 = 72.47

You can appreciate what a single wild 'outlier' will do to a
neat data set and why statisticians are mortally suspicious
of them!

Chapter 4

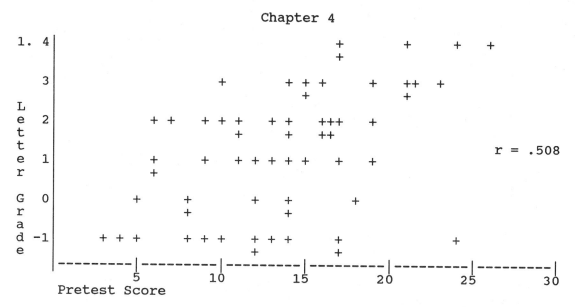

Pretest Score

A significant correlation exists between PRETEST score and
FINAL LETTER GRADE. Obviously, the correlation is not perfect.
Several factors must be considered: motivation of students in
a General Mathematics course to excel, the grading and testing
procedures of individual instructors, et. al.

One last warning: A measure of positive correlation does NOT
imply CAUSE. Obviously, an increase in ACT score does NOT
CAUSE an increase in Pretest score. We don't know that the
next candidate who walks in the door with ACT score in hand
will score well or poorly on the Pretest. He might come in
with a ACT score of 8 (out of 36) and score a perfect 30 on
the Pretest (one student in our group did!), or come in with
an ACT score of 21 and do merely fair on the Pretest. (One
student with an ACT of 21 scored 20 out of 30 - or 67% - on
the Pretest, a score that was below the 70% needed to continue
in the course. Help sessions and retests were offered: this
student did continue and eventually managed a respectable B
in the course.)

2. A scatter diagram look like this:

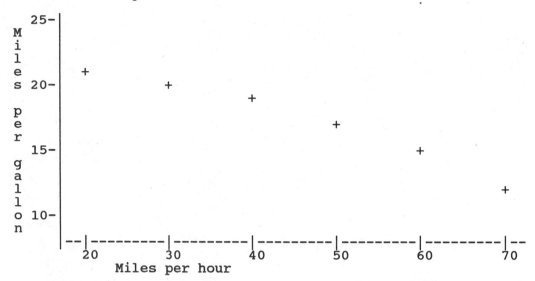

Miles per hour

Obviously, as speed INcreases, the number of miles per gallon
of fuel DEcreases. Assuming linearity (a questionable assumption), we find the correlation coefficient. Again, resorting
to our calculator, we find r = -.9863. The negative sign is
our indication that, as the table verifies, increased speed
yields diminished efficiency. That we're quite close to -1
indicates an almost perfect linear relationship. But, be
careful! This last may be a reflection of limited data.

3. Such rankings are ORDINAL data. One question: are these two
   instructors in essential agreement? The obvious answer is no.
   The text ranked first by one instructor is ranked third by the
   other. They are in disagreement on each and every text - a
   not unusual predicament (and you thought teaching was fun!).

   There is a measure, r(s), which correlates such ordinal data by
   rank. We find

$$r(s) = 1 - \frac{6\ SUM\ d^2}{n(n^2 - 1)} = 1 - \frac{6(36)}{8(63)} = 1 - \frac{3}{7} = \frac{4}{7} = .5714$$

   a not unexpectedly low correlation score. [By Table 4.4, a
   significant value for r would be .707 or better.]

   Note that if we compute r instead of r(s), considering the
   pairs of rankings as pairs of scores, we get precisely the
   same value, r = .5714. Does this always work? No, but it
   tends to do so as n increases and, as in this case, where
   there are no (or few) matching rankings.

Chapter 5

$$r) = \frac{30}{45} = \frac{2}{3}. \qquad b) \; P(So) = \frac{10}{45} = \frac{2}{9}.$$

$$c) \; P(F') = 1 - P(F) = 1 - \frac{2}{3} = \frac{1}{3}.$$

2. Let A = student is under 20, B = student is over 30
      M = student is a male,   F = student is a female

a) $P(A) = \dfrac{48}{100} = \dfrac{12}{25} = .48;$ \qquad b) $P(F) = \dfrac{37}{100} = .37$

c) $P(M) = 1 - .37 = .63;$ \qquad d) $P(M \text{ and } A) = \dfrac{26}{100} = .26$

e) $P(M \text{ or } A) = \dfrac{63}{100} + \dfrac{48}{100} - \dfrac{26}{100} = \dfrac{85}{100} = .85$

f) $P(M|B) = \dfrac{P(M \text{ and } B)}{P(B)} = \dfrac{16/100}{25/100} = \dfrac{16}{25} = .64$

g) Since $P(M|A) = \dfrac{26}{48}$ and $P(M) = \dfrac{26}{100}$, $P(M|A) =\!/ P(M)$, events
      M and A are not independent.

h) Since $P(M \text{ and } A) = \dfrac{26}{100} =\!/ 0$, events M and A are not
      mutually exclusive.

3. a) $\dfrac{33}{105} = \dfrac{11}{35} = .314;$ \qquad b) $\dfrac{12}{105} = \dfrac{4}{35} = .114;$

c) Note that $P(Fr \text{ and } So) = 0$; the events are mutually exclusive

d) $P(Fr) = \dfrac{4}{35} = .114$ and $P(So) = \dfrac{15}{105} = \dfrac{1}{7} = .143$, so that

   $P(Fr) \; P(So) = .016 =\!/ 0 = P(Fr \text{ and } So)$. The events are
   not independent.

4. a)

	(C')	(C)	
(I) Immediate Area	38	35	73
(O) Out of state	18	9	27
	56	44	100

b) (i) $P(C|I) = \dfrac{35}{73}$ (ii) $P(O|C') = \dfrac{18}{56}$ (iii) $P(I|C) = \dfrac{35}{44}$

(iv) $P(C'|O) = \dfrac{18}{27} = \dfrac{2}{3}$

5. a) $P(A') = 1 - P(A) = 1 - .40 = .60$

b) $P(A|B) = \dfrac{P(A \text{ and } B)}{P(B)} = \dfrac{25}{70} = .357$

c) $P(A \text{ or } B) = P(A) + P(B) - P(A \text{ and } B) = .4 + .7 - .25 = .85$

d) $P(B|A) = \dfrac{P(B \text{ and } A)}{P(A)} = \dfrac{25}{40} = .625$

e) $P(A \text{ and } B) \neq 0$. Events are not mutually exclusive.

f) $P(A|B) = \dfrac{5}{14} = .357$ and $P(A) = .4$; events are not independent.

g) $P[(A \text{ and } B)'] = 1 - P(A \text{ and } B) = 1 - .25 = .75$ [Note also
    that $P[(A \text{ and } B)'] = P(A' \text{ or } B')$.]

h) $P(A' \text{ and } B') = P[(A \text{ or } B)'] = 1 - .85 = .15$

i) $P[(A \text{ or } B)'] = .15$ [See (h)]

j) $P(A' \text{ or } B') = .75$ [See (g)]

k) $P(A|B') = \dfrac{P(A \text{ and } B')}{P(B')} = \dfrac{15}{30} = .5$

l) $P(B|A') = \dfrac{P(B \text{ and } A')}{P(A')} = \dfrac{45}{60} = .75$

m) $P(A'|B') = \dfrac{P(A' \text{ and } B')}{P(B')} = \dfrac{15}{30} = .5$

6. a)   (i) P(A or B or C) = P(A) + P(B) + P(C) = .4 + .2 + .1 = .7

         (ii) P[(A or B or C)'] = 1 - .7 = .3

        (iii) P(A and C) = 0

         (iv) P(A' and C') = .5   [Note: Two events may be mutually exclusive, but their complements need not be.]

   b)   (i) P(A and B) = .06

         (ii) P(A and C) = .04

        (iii) P(B and C) = .02

         (iv) P(A and B and C) = (.4)(.2)(.1) = .006

          (v) P(A and B and C') = .054

         (vi) P(A and B' and C) = .034

        (vii) P(A' and B and C) = .014

       (viii) P(A and B' and C') = .306

         (ix) P(A' and B and C') = .132

          (x) P(A' and B' and C) = .046

         (xi) P[(A and B and C)'] = 1 - .006 = .994

        (xii) P(A' and B' and C') = P[(A or B or C)'] = .408

7. By the 'multiplication rule,' 5x6x7 = 210.

8. C(12,3) = 220.

9. C(12,3) = 220

10. a) 11!   b) 9x10!   c) 10!

11. a) C(3,3)C(9,0)/C(12,3) = 1/220 = .0045

    b) C(1,1)C(11,2)/C(12,3) = 1/4 = .25

12. P(W) = P(W and F) + P(W and F')

         = P(F)P(W|F) + P(F')P(W|F')

         = (.42)(.74) + (.58)(.08) = .3524

13. $P(TB|Pos) = \dfrac{P(TB \text{ and } Pos)}{P(Pos)} = \dfrac{P(Pos \text{ and } TB)}{P(Pos \text{ and } TB) + P(Pos \text{ and } TB')}$

$= \dfrac{P(Pos|TB)\,P(TB)}{P(Pos|TB)\,P(TB) + P(Pos|TB')\,P(TB')}$

$= \dfrac{(.75)(.01)}{(.75)(.01) + (.25)(.99)} = \dfrac{.0075}{.255} = .0294 = .03$

Chapter 6

```
                Half dollar
                     y
1.                |  0   |   1         P(Coins match) = P(0,0) + P(1,1)
            --   |----- |----
       Q     0  | .25  |  .25                = .5
       t  x  -- |----- |----
       r     1  | .25  |  .25
```

2.   P(x = 4) = 1/5   P(x = 1,3,5) = 3/5

$$\frac{2 + 5 + 8 + 11}{26} = 1$$

3. Yes, this is a probability distribution:

$$P(x = 2 \text{ or } 8) = \frac{2 + 8}{26} = \frac{10}{26} = .3846$$

                                Note: .3846 + .6154 = 1

$$P(x = 5 \text{ or } 11) = \frac{5 + 11}{26} = \frac{16}{26} = .6154$$

4. P(x = 0) = .36   P(x = 1) = .48   P(x = 2) = .16

5. P(x = 0) = .333   P(x = 1) = .533   P(x = 2) = .133

6. For #4, MU = 0(.36) + 1(.48) + 2(.16) = .8

   SIGMA^2 = 0(.36) + 1(.48) + 4(.16) = .48

   For #5, MU = 0(.33) + 1(.53) + 2(.13) = .8

   SIGMA^2 = 0(.33) + 1(.53 + 4(.13) = .427

7. MU = 0(.2) + 1(.2) + 2(.2) + 3(.2) + 4(.2) + 5(.2) = 3.0

   SIGMA^2 = [0(.2)+1(.2)+4(.2)+9(.2)+16(.2)+25(.2)] - 9 = 2.0

8. MU = 2(2/26) + 5(5/26) + 8(8/26) + 11(11/26) = 8.231

   SIGMA^2 = 4(2/26)+25(5/26)+64(8/26)+121(11/26) - 8.231^2

           = 76 - 67.7456 = 8.2544

   SIGMA = 2.873

9. (i) P(SSSFF) = [(1/3)^3][(2/3)^2] = 4/243 = .01646

   (ii) P(x = 3) = C(5,3)[(1/3)^3][(2/3)^2] = .1646

10. (i) P(x = 6) = C(10,6)[(1/4)^6][(3/4)^4] = .0162

    (ii) P(x > 6) = C(10,6)[(1/4)^6][(3/4)^4] + ...
                        + C(10,10)[(1/4)^0][(3/4)^10] = .0197

    MU = np = 10(1/3) = 3.33

    SIGMA^2 = npq = np(1-p) = 10(1/3)(2/3) = 2.22

    SIGMA = 1.491

11. MU = np = 12(.18) = 2.16

    SIGMA^2 = np(1-p) = 12(.18)(.82) = 1.7712

    SIGMA = 1.33

12. (i) C(5,5)C(7,0)/C(12,5) = 1/792 = .0013

    (ii) C(2,2)C(10,3)/C(12,5) = 120/792 = .15

    (iii) C(2,1)C(10,4)/C(12,5) = (2)(210)/792 = .53.   So, then,
          P(A or B) = P(A) + P(B) - P(A and B) = .53 + .53 - .15
          = .909

13. (i) C(25,8)C(5,2)/C(30,10) = .36

    (ii) 1 - C(25,10)C(5,0)/C(30,10) = 1 - .1088 = .8912

    (iii) MU = nk/N = (10)(5)/30 = 1.67

$$SIGMA^2 = k(N-k)(n)(N-n)/(N^2)(N-1) = \frac{(5)(25)(10)(20)}{(900)(29)}$$

$$= .958$$

    SIGMA = .979

14. (i) $P(3) = \dfrac{(3^3)(e^{-3})}{3!} = .224$ (ii) $P(0) = \dfrac{(3^0)(e^{-3})}{0!} = .05$

    (iii) 1 - P(0) = 1 - .05 = .95   (iv) P(3) + P(4) + ...

          = 1 - [P(0)+P(1)+P(2)] = 1 - [.05+.15+.224] = .5768

15. (i) C(11,1)C(239,11)/C(240,12) = .05

Chapter 7

1. Height: [4.5 - (-1.5)]h = 1, h = 1/6

   P(x > 1.5) = (4.5 - 1.5))(1/6) = 1/2

   Mean: (-1.5 + 4.5)/2 = 1.5

   Standard deviation: [4.5 - (-1.5)]/SQRT(12) = 1.732

2. Height: [(10 - 0) + (40 - 30)]h = 1, h = 1/20

   P(35 < x < 40) = 5(1/20) = 1/4

   Mean: (5 + 35)/2 = 20

   Standard deviation: [(10 - 0) + (40 - 30)]/SQRT(12) = 5.77

3. (i) P(-1.5 < z < 0) + P(0 < z < .5) = .4332 + .1915 = .6247

   (ii) P(0 < z < 1.56) - P(0 < z < .56) = .4406 - .2123 = .2283

   (iii) P(z > 1.44) = .5 - P(z < 1.44) = .5 - .4251 = .0749

   (iv) P(z < -.47) = P(z > .47) = .5-P(z < .47) = .5-.1808 = .3192

   (v) P(-z < Z < z) = .5 implies P(0 < Z < z) = .25, so that
       .67 < z < .68. We could interpolate: P(0<Z<.67) = .2486
       and P(0<Z<.68) = .2517. It follows that P(0<Z<.67x) = .25
       where x/10 = 14/31 [.25-.2486=.0014 and .2517-.2486=.0031]
       so x = 4.51 or 5. Thus, P(0 < Z < .675) = .2500, to the
       nearest thousandths.

4.   (i) $P(52 < X < 76) = P(\dfrac{52 - 70}{12} < Z < \dfrac{76 - 70}{12}) = P(-1.5 < Z < .5)$

     $= .6247$ [See #3(i)]

     $P(76.72 < X < 88.72) = P(\dfrac{76.72 - 70}{12} < Z < \dfrac{88.72 - 70}{12})$

     $(.56 < Z < 1.56) = .2283$ [See #3(ii)]

     $P(X > 87.28) = P(Z > \dfrac{87.28 - 70}{12}) = P(Z > 1.44) = .0749$
         [See #3(iii)]

     $P(X < 64.36) = P(Z < \dfrac{64.36 - 70}{12}) = P(Z < -.47) = .3192$
         [See #3(iv)]

     $P(-x < X < x) = .5$: As in #3(v), $P(0 < X < x) = .25$, which
        is equivalent to $P(0 < Z < z) = .25$, which [by #3(v)],
        yields $z = .675$. Now, $x = 70 + 12(.675) = 78.1$

  (ii) $P(X > x) = .15$ is equivalent to $P(0 < X < x) = .35$, which,
        again, is equivalent to $P(0 < Z < z) = .35$, for

$$z = \dfrac{x - 70}{12}$$

     From Table A-4, $z = 1.04$ [the table entry is .3508], and
        so $x = 70 + 12(1.04) = 82.48$.

5. $\bar{x} = 69.8$, $s = 16.82$

   Twenty of 29 or 69% are within one standard deviation; 28 of 29,
      or 96.6% are within two standard deviations of the mean.

6. $P(x > 8) = P(x = 9) + P(x = 10) = C(10,9)(.4^9)(.6)$
                                      $+ C(10,10)(.4^{10}) = .00168$

   $P(X > 8.5) = P(Z > \dfrac{8.5 - 4}{1.55}) = P(Z > 2.905) = .5 - .49815 = .00185$

   $MU = np = 10(.4) = 4$ $SIGMA^2 = np(1-p) = 4(.6) = 2.4$
                                      $SIGMA = 1.55$

7. MU = np = 120(.4) = 48   SIGMA = SQRT[48(.6)] = 5.37

$$P(X > 96) = P(Z > \frac{96 - 48}{5.37}) = P(Z > 8.9443) = 0$$

8. MU = 6 = 1/A $P(X > 1/4) = e^{[(-1/6)(1/4)]} = e^{[-1/14]} = .96$

$$P(X<1/12) = 1 - P(X>1/12) = 1 - e^{[(-1/6)(1/12)]}$$
$$= 1 - e^{(-1/72)} = .0138$$

9. MU = 48 = 1/A $P(X < 3) = 1 - P(X > 3) = 1 - e^{[(-1/48)(3)]}$
$$= 1 - e^{(-1/16)} = .0606$$

10. MU = 16 = 1/A $P(X < 18) = 1 - P(X > 18) = 1 - e^{[(-1/16)(18)]}$
$$= 1 - e^{(-9/8)} = 1 - .325 = .675$$

Chapter 8

1. a) $P(\bar{x} > 56) = P(z > \dfrac{56 - 50}{10/SQRT(12)}) = P(z > \dfrac{6}{2.88675}) = P(z > 2.08)$
   $= .5 - .4812 = .0188$ or 1.88%

   b) $P(\bar{x} > 44) = P(z > \dfrac{44 - 50}{10/SQRT(12)}) = P(z > -2.08) = .5 + .4812 =$
   $.9812$ or 98.12%

   c) $P(44 < \bar{x} < 56) = P(\dfrac{44 - 50}{10/SQRT(12)} < z < \dfrac{56 - 50}{10/SQRT(12)})$

   $P(-2.08 < z < 2.08) = 2(.4812) = .9624$ or 96.24%

   d) $P(\bar{x} < 44) = P(z < \dfrac{44 - 50}{10/SQRT(12)}) = P(z < -2.08) = .5 - .4812$
   $= .0188$ or 1.88% [See (a)]

   e) $P(\bar{x} > 56) + P(44 < \bar{x} < 56) + P(\bar{x} < 44) = 2(.0188) + .9624 =$
   $.0376 + .9624 = 1.0000$

2. $P(\bar{x} < 62.3) = P(z < \dfrac{62.3 - 73.1}{16.3/SQRT(27)}) = P(z < \dfrac{-10.8}{3.137}) = P(z < -3.44)$
   $= .5 = .4997 = .0003.$ [New instructors are often notorious
   for carrying their graduate school demands with them.]

3. $SIGMA = [SQRT(10)](4.2797)/\{SQRT[(69-10)/(69-1)]\}$

   $= [3.1623](4.2797)/\{.9315\} = 14.5292$

   Without the correction factor, we predict

   $$SIGMA = 4.2797[SQRT(10)] = 13.5336$$

   The correction factor for finite population provides some
   improvement.

4. $MU(\overline{x}) = 17.75$ $SIGMA(\overline{x}) = 2.24$ Discrepancy is probably
   due to round-off error: $(57395 - 53116)/237.6 = 18.01$

   Means would be distributed normally if driving habits remain
   relatively constant throughout each 3-month period.

5. $P(MU > 20) = P(z > \dfrac{20 - 17.75}{2.24}) = P(z > 1.00) = .5 - .3413 =$
   .1587 or 15.87%

   $P(MU < 16) = P(z < \dfrac{16 - 17.75}{2.24}) = P(z < -.78) = .5 - .2823 =$
   .2177 or 21.77%

6. $P\{17.75-1.28[2.24/SQRT(13)] < MU < 17.75+1.28[2.24/SQRT(13)]\}$

   $= P(17.75-.7952 < MU < 17.75+.7952)$

   $= P(16.955 < MU < 18.545) = .80$

   $P\{17.75-1.645[2.24/SQRT(13)] < MU < 17.75+1.645[2.24/SQRT(13)]\}$

   $= P(17.75-1.022 < MU < 17.75+1.022)$

   $= P(16.728 < MU < 18.772) = .90$

   The interval increases in size as we go from 80% CI to 90% CI.
   We have to given ourselves broader latitude--a larger interval, from which to choose our Mean if we're to increase confidence.

7. For an 80% CI, we want $t(.10,12) = 1.356$, and

   $P\{17.75-1.356[2.24/SQRT(13)] < MU < 17.75+1.356[2.24/SQRT(13)]\}$

   $= P(17.75-.8424 < MU < 17.75+.8424)$

   $= P(16.91 < MU < 18.59) = .80$

   For a 90% CI, we want $t(.05,12) = 1.782$, and

   $P\{17.75-1.782[2.24/SQRT(13)] < MU < 17.75+1.782[2.24/SQRT(13)]\}$

   $= P(17.75-1.107 < MU < 17.75+1.107)$

   $= P(16.643 < MU < 18.857) = .90$

8.   (i) $n = \left[\dfrac{(1.645)(15)}{5}\right]^2 = 24.354.$ So $n = 25$

   (ii) $n = \left[\dfrac{(1.645)(2.24)}{5}\right]^2 = .543.$ So $n = 1(!)$

   (iii) $n = \left[\dfrac{(1.96)(2.24)}{5}\right]^2 = 3.08.$ So $n = 4$

Chapter 9

1. $(\overline{x} - MU)/[SIGMA/SQRT(n)] = (20.8 - 19.4)/[3.6/SQRT(60)] =$

   $1.4/.4648 = 3.01$.   Since $3.01 > 1.96$, we reject the Null

   Hypothesis, $H(o)$.

2. For $z = 3.01$, the area under the Normal curve in the right tail

   is $.5 - .4981 = .0013 = p$.   Since $p < .01$, we reject the

   Null, once again.

3. $x = 19.4 +/- 1.96[3.6/SQRT(60)] = 19.4 +/- .911$, for limits:

   18.489 or 20.311.   Now, $z = (20.311 - 20.8)/[36/SQRT(60)]$

   $= -1.05$, so that the corresponding $BETA = .5 - .3531 = .147$.

   Further, $POWER = 1 - BETA = 1 - .147 = .853$.

   We note that the remainder of the region under the Normal curve
   specified by $ALPHA = .05$ lies to the left:

$$(18.489 - 20.8)/[3.6/SQRT(60)] = -4.97$$

   The area to the left of which [Table A-4] is essentially zero

4. Since the scores are Normally distributed, the mean would be
   'near' the midpoint of the interval. We'll take

$$MU = (36 + 112)/2 = 74$$

   The standard deviation will be 'near' the value

$$SIGMA = Range/4 = (112 - 36)/4 = 19$$

   Our test, then, is $z = (\overline{x} - MU)/[SIGMA/SQRT(n)]$, so that our
   computed

$$Z* = \frac{80 - 74}{19/SQRT(64)} = \frac{6}{19/SQRT(64)} = 2.5263$$

Since ALPHA = .10, ALPHA/2 = .05 and z = 1.645. Further, Z* > z, so we reject our Null hypothesis. But we do so with some hesitancy. The paucity of information says suspend judgment!

5. Z* = (12.07 - 14.24)/[8.49/SQRT(143)] = -3.0565. Since our compute Z* < -1.645, the Z-value for ALPHA = .05 and a ONE-TAIL test, we reject the Null hypothesis.

6. Our Standard deviation for finite population,

$$s(\bar{x}) = \frac{13.7}{SQRT(45)}[SQRT(\frac{125 - 45}{125 - 1})] = 1.64$$

$$\text{Our computed } Z* = \frac{\bar{x} - MU}{s(x)} = \frac{76.4 - 73.6}{1.64} = 1.7073, \text{ while for}$$

ALPHA = .05, z = 1.645. Since our compute Z* > z, we reject our Null hypothesis. (But we note that our p-VALUE = .0436, a less than overwhelming cause for rejection; the experimental group did somewhat better.

7. Our statistic, t = ($\bar{x}$ - MU)/[s/SQRT(n)] = (43-46)/[2.5/SQRT(12)]

= -4.157, while t(.025,11) = 2.201; we reject the new batch

as evidently inferior.

8. Our statistic, t* = (36.4 - 40)/[8.8/SQRT(18)] = -1.7356, while

t(.05,17) = -1.740. Since t* > t, we fail to reject H(o).

With the finite population adjustment, $SQRT[\frac{200 - 18}{200 - 1}] = .9563$

our Standard deviation becomes s = 1.9836, and t* = -1.815

and t* < t(.05,17). We reject H(o).

9. $CHI^2 = \frac{(18 - 1)s^2}{100} = \frac{17(8.8^2)}{100} = 13.1648.$ Our table value for

CHI^2(.1,17) = 24.7690.   Since our computed CHI^2 < 24.769, we fail to reject H(o).

10. Our computed CHI^2 = $\dfrac{(18 - 1)(8.8^\wedge 2)}{49}$ = 26.867, while the table value for CHI^2(.1,17) = 24.7690.   Since 26.867 > 24.769, we reject H(o).

Chapter 10

1. a) $P\{(28.3 - 25.4) - 1.96(SQRT[\dfrac{4.3^2}{45} + \dfrac{5.1^2}{40}]) < MU(1) - MU(2)$

$< (28.3 - 25.4) + 1.96(SQRT[\dfrac{4.3^2}{45} + \dfrac{5.1^2}{40}])\}$

$= P\{2.9 - 1.96(1.03) < MU(1) - MU(2) < 2.9 + 1.96(1.03)\}$

$= P\{2.9 - 2.02 < MU(1) - MU(2) < 2.9 + 2.02\}$

$= P\{.88 < MU(1) - MU(2) < 3.92\} = .95$

b) $n = 2.58[4.3^2 + 5.1^2]/4 = 28.7$ implies $n = 29$.

c) H(o): MU(1) = MU(2), H(a): MU(1) =/ MU(2)

$$Z* = \dfrac{28.3 - 25.4}{SQRT[\dfrac{4.3^2}{45} + \dfrac{5.1^2}{40}]} = \dfrac{2.9}{1.03} = 2.815$$

Z(ALPHA/2) = Z(.025) = 1.96, so Z* > Z(.025) and we reject the Null hypothesis.

d) p = .5 - .49755 = .00245

e) Computations comparable to those in (c) yield

$$\dfrac{2.9}{SQRT[\dfrac{4.3^2}{20} + \dfrac{5.1^2}{20}]} = \dfrac{2.9}{1.49164} = 1.944$$

This time 1.944 < 1.96, and we fail to reject the Null.

f) $P\{2.9 - 2.58(SQRT[\dfrac{4.3^2}{45} + \dfrac{5.1^2}{40}]) < MU(1) - MU(2) <$

$2.9 + 2.58(SQRT[\dfrac{4.3^2}{45} + \dfrac{5.1^2}{40}])\}$

$$= P\{2.9 - 2.58(1.03) < MU(1) - MU(2) < 2.9 + 2.58(1.03)\}$$

$$= P\{.2423 < MU(1) - MU(2) < 5.5577\} = .99$$

The interval here is LARGER, to give us assurance we've 'captured' MU(1) - MU(2).

g) The test results is as in (e): t* = 1.944, but t(.025,36) = 2.029 (with a bit of interpolation), where

$$df = \cfrac{\left[\cfrac{4.3^2}{20} + \cfrac{5.1^2}{20}\right]}{\cfrac{\left[\cfrac{4.3^2}{20}\right]^2}{19} + \cfrac{\left[\cfrac{5.1^2}{20}\right]^2}{19}}$$

Here, t'* < t', and we again fail to reject the Null.

h) s(p)^2 = {[n(1)-1]s(1)^2 + [n(2)-1]s(2)^2}/[n(1)+n(2)-2]

$$= \{19(4.3^2) + 19(5.1^2)\}/[20 + 20 - 2]$$

$$= 22.25$$

while, t' = [$\overline{x}$(1) - $\overline{x}$(2)]/s(p){SQRT[1/n(1) + 1/n(2)]}

$$= 2.9/(4.717)\{SQRT[1/20 + 1/20]\}$$

$$= 2.9/1.4916 = 1.944$$

Our CI is [2.9 - t(.025,38)(4.717)(.316) < MU(1) - MU(2) <

$$2.9 + t(.025,38)(4.717)(.316)]$$

$$= [2.9 - (2.025)(4.717)(.316) < MU(1) - MU(2) <$$

$$2.9 + (2.025)(4.717).316)]$$

$$= [2.9 - 3.0184 < MU(1) - MU(2) < 2.9 + 3.0184]$$

$$= [-.1184 < MU(1) - MU(2) < 5.9184]$$

and, again, we cannot preclude MU(1) = MU(2), and so fail to reject the Null.

(i) Our s(1) = 4.3 and s(2) = 5.1, so $F* = \dfrac{s(2)^2}{s(1)^2} = \dfrac{5.1^2}{4.3^2} = 1.41$

From the table, F[ALPHA/2,NU(1),NU(2)] = F(.025,44,39)= 1.51

Since F* < F(.025,44,39), we fail to reject the Null.

(j) F(LOWER) = 1/F(.025,39,44) = 1/1.51 = .66

F(UPPER) = F(.025,44,39) = 1.51, and the CI is given by

$$\left[\frac{s(2)^2/s(1)^2}{F(U)}, \frac{s(2)^2/s(1)^2}{F(L)}\right] = \left[\frac{1.4067}{1.51}, \frac{1.4067}{.66}\right]$$

$$= (.9316, 2.1314)$$

Thus, it's possible that SIGMA(1)^2 = SIGMA(2)^2, since our interval contains 1.

(k) Our F* remains: F* = 1.4067. F[ALPHA/2,NU(1),NU(2)] = F[.025,19,19] = 1.82 and F* < F[.025,19,19] and we again fail to reject the Null.

For the Confidence Interval, F(LOWER) = 1/F(.025,19,19) = 1/1.82 = .55, and F(UPPER) = F(.025,19,19) = 1.82. So

$$\left[\frac{s(2)^2/s(1)^2}{F(U)}, \frac{s(2)^2/s(1)^2}{F(L)}\right] = \left[\frac{1.4067}{1.82}, \frac{1.4067}{.55}\right]$$

$$= [.773, 2.558]$$

2. Postest - Pretest differences:

- 5	-12	3	-12	-16	$\bar{d}$ = -11.2
- 4	-10	-27	-15	-28	
- 9	-22	-25	1	-13	s = 11.6082
-29	- 9	15	-15	-13	
- 5	- 5	1	5	-31	s^2 = 134.75

At ALPHA = .05, t(ALPHA/2,24) = 2.064, and our computed

$$t = \frac{-11.2}{11.6082/\text{SQRT}(25)} = -4.824$$

and our CI is {-11.2 - (2.064)[$\dfrac{11.6082}{SQRT(25)}$] < MU(Pre)-MU(Post) <

$\qquad\qquad\qquad\qquad\qquad$ -11.2 + (2.064)[$\dfrac{11.6082}{SQRT(25)}$]}

$\qquad$ = {-11.2 - 4.792 < MU(Pre)-MU(Post) < -11.2 + 4.792}

$\qquad$ = {-15.992 < MU(Pre) - MU(Post) < -6.408

which does NOT contain the zero.

The corresponding test of hypothesis is

$\quad$ H(o): MU(1) = MU(2) and H(a): MU(1) =/ MU(2) with

test statistic, t = $\dfrac{MU(1) - MU(2)}{s(d)/SQRT(n)}$ = -4.824. Tested against

t(.025,24) + 2.064. Since |-4.824| > 2.064, we reject the

Null: the means are not equal. There is reason to believe

the Pretest is not a valid predictor of success.

Chapter 11

1. Confidence Interval for passing the course, ALPHA = .05, n = 90

$$P\left\{\frac{44}{90} - 1.96\left[\text{SQRT}\left(\frac{\frac{44}{90}\left(1 - \frac{44}{90}\right)}{90}\right)\right] < p < \frac{44}{90} + 1.96\left[\text{SQRT}\left(\frac{\frac{44}{90}\left(1 - \frac{44}{90}\right)}{90}\right)\right]\right\}$$

= P{.489 - 1.96(.0527) < p < .489 + 1.96(.0527)}

= P{.3857 < p < .5923} = .95

2. Confidence Interval for passing the course, ALPHA = .05, n = 75

$$P\left\{\frac{44}{75} - 1.96\left[\text{SQRT}\left(\frac{\frac{44}{75}\left(1 - \frac{44}{75}\right)}{75}\right)\right] < p < \frac{44}{75} + 1.96\left[\text{SQRT}\left(\frac{\frac{44}{75}\left(1 - \frac{44}{75}\right)}{75}\right)\right]\right\}$$

= P{.5867 - 1.96(.0569) < p < .5867 + 1.96(.0569)}

= P{.475 < p < .698} = .95

3. No matter how you contrive to analyze the results, something between half to two-fifths of the students fail. Since the mathematical demands are minimal--and we're dealing with the 'better' high school graduates from the area--there is reason for alarm: and need for colloquy.

4. Since 21/30 is passing, p(0) = .70. From Table A-8, the Confidence Interval for ALPHA = .05 has limits

p(L) = .428 and p(U) = .945

and so, p(L) < p(0) < p(U). We thus fail to reject H(o): p = p(0). We're claiming some 75% will pass; but look at the width of the interval. The small sample may not reflect the population very well, but it's not in dire conflict either.

5. Your data; your game.

6. p = .45, n = 150.   a) A 95% CI for p:

$$P\{.45 - 1.96SQRT[\frac{(.45)(.55)}{150}] < p < .45 + 1.96SQRT[\frac{(.45)(.55)}{150}]\}$$

   = P{.45 - 1.96(.0406) < p < .45 + 1.96(.0406)}

   = P{.37 < p < .53} = .95

   b) Max'm Error = $1.96SQRT[\frac{(.45)(.55)}{150}]$ = 1.96(.0406) = .08

7. a) $P\{.45-2.58SQRT[\frac{(.45)(.55)}{150}] < p < .45+2.58SQRT[\frac{(.45)(.55)}{150}]\}$

   = P{.45 - .1048 < p < .45 + .1048}

   = P{.345 < p < .555} = .99

   b) $P\{.45-1.645SQRT[\frac{(.45)(.55)}{150}] < p < .45+1.645SQRT[\frac{(.45)(.55)}{150}]\}$

   = P{.45 - .0668 < p < .45 + .0668}

   = P{.383 < p < .517} = .90

The Confidence Interval increases (decreases) in breadth as our
   confidence increases (decreases).

8. p = .45, n = 15

$$P\{.45-1.96SQRT[\frac{(.45)(.55)}{15}] < p < .45+1.96SQRT[\frac{(.45)(.55)}{15}]\}$$

   = P{.45 - .2518 < p < .45 + .2518}

   = P{.198 < p < .702} = .95

An interval (in #6) of width .16 has becomes (in #8) an interval
   of width .504; depending on the circumstances, this last
   could be a useless bit of information: the sample size may
   be too small to reflect the population.

Chapter 12

1. Our three classes appear as follows:

I	II	III
97	92	85
83	91	73
94	96	76
93	88	70
63	78	98
63	91	70
98	73	78
94	71	72
---	---	---
685	680	622

$$T(Total) = 685 + 680 + 622 = 1987$$

For our ANOVA, we need

$$SS(Factor) = \left[\frac{685^2}{8} + \frac{680^2}{8} + \frac{622^2}{8}\right] - \frac{1987^2}{24} = 306.583$$

$$SS(Total) = [97^2 + 83^2 + ... + 72^2] - \frac{1987^2}{24} = 3095.958$$

$$SS(Error) = SS(Total) - SS(Factor) = 2789.375$$

$$MS(Factor) = \frac{SS(Factor)}{k-1} = \frac{306.583}{2} = 153.292$$

$$MS(Error) = \frac{SS(Error)}{n-k} = \frac{3095.958}{21} = 147.427$$

$$F = \frac{MS(Factor)}{MS(Error)} = \frac{153.292}{147.427} = 1.04$$

Our computed F* < F(.1,2,21) = 2.57, indicating that better
    students are more predictable (remember our Scatter Diagram
    from earlier chapters?)

2. Let's reproduce our table with cell totals:

	Freshmen	Upperclassmen	
Male	521	463	984
Female	517	486	1003
	1038	949	1987

Then, for our ANOVA, we need:

$$SSA = \frac{1}{12}[T(Males)^2 + T(Females)^2] - \frac{T^2}{24}$$

$$= \frac{1}{12}[984^2 + 1003^2] - \frac{1987^2}{24} = 15.04$$

$$SSB = \frac{1}{12}[T(Freshmen)^2 + T(Upperclassmen)^2] - \frac{T^2}{24}$$

$$= \frac{1}{12}[1038^2 + 949^2] - \frac{1987^2}{24} = 330.04$$

$$SSAB = \frac{1}{6}[SUM(Cell\ totals)^2] - SSA - SSB - \frac{T^2}{24}$$

$$\frac{1}{6}[989295] - 15.04 - 330.04 - \frac{1987^2}{24} = 30.378$$

$$SST = SUM(Scores^2 - \frac{T^2}{24} = 167603 - 164507.04 = 3095.96$$

$$SSE = SST - SSA - SSB - SSAB = 3095.96-15.04-330.04-30.378$$

$$= 2720.51$$

So, then, $MSA = \frac{SSA}{a-1} = \frac{15.04}{1} = 15.04$

$$MSB = \frac{SSB}{b-1} = \frac{330.04}{1} = 330.04$$

$$MSAB = \frac{SSAB}{(a-1)(b-1)} = 30.37$$

$$MSE = \frac{SSE}{ab(r-1)} = \frac{2720.51}{20} = 136.0255$$

Finally, $F(1) = \frac{MSA}{MSE} = \frac{15.04}{136.0255} = .1106$

$$F(2) = \frac{MSB}{MSE} = \frac{330.04}{136.0255} = 2.426$$

$$F(3) = \frac{MSAB}{MSE} = \frac{30.37}{136.0255} = .223$$

-- each to be compared against $F(.1,1,20) = 2.97$, with the appropriate conclusions.

Chapter 13

1. Let's reproduce the table with the agency's expectations added:

	Hawaii	Japan	Himalayas	
Men	26(40)	13(40)	61(20)	100
Women	59(40)	29(40)	12(20)	100
	85(80)	42(80)	72(40)	200

The CHI^2 computation is the following:

$$CHI^2 = \frac{(85-80)^2}{80} + \frac{(42-80)^2}{80} + \frac{(73-40)^2}{40} = 45.5875$$

and the corresponding table value, CHI^2(.1,2) = 4.605

Obviously, the agency's expectations -- and experience of past years -- don't match current desires. Either additional data must be sought or adjustments made in travel and hotal accommodations.

2. The table, with cell expectations inserted, is reproduced as follows:

	Hawaii (H)	Japan (J)	Himalayas (Him)	
Men (M)	26 (42.5)	13 (21.0)	61 (36.5)	100
Women (W)	59 (42.5)	29 (21.0)	12 (36.5)	100
	85	42	73	200

The expectations are computed, as indicated:

$$E(MH) = \frac{100 \cdot 85}{200} = 42.5 \quad E(MJ) = \frac{100 \cdot 42}{200} = 21.0 \quad E(MHim) = \frac{100 \cdot 73}{200} = 36.5$$

$$E(WH) = \frac{100 \cdot 85}{200} = 42.5 \quad E(WJ) = \frac{100 \cdot 42}{200} = 21.0 \quad E(WHim) = \frac{100 \cdot 73}{200} = 36.5$$

and the CHI^2 value:

$$CHI^2 = \frac{(26-42.5)^2}{42.5} + \frac{(13-21)^2}{21} + \frac{(61-36.5)^2}{36.5}$$

$$+ \frac{(59-42.5)^2}{42.5} + \frac{(29-21)^2}{21} + \frac{(12-36.5)^2}{36.5} = 51.797$$

The corresponding table entry: CHI^2(.1,2) = 4.605

Once again, the agency has problems that need attention. But we need more information: who makes travel decisions for the family? Should we expect male dominance -- and so book for high adventure? or female dominance -- and book for a luau?

Chapter 14

1. The Scatter Diagram for the data looks like this:

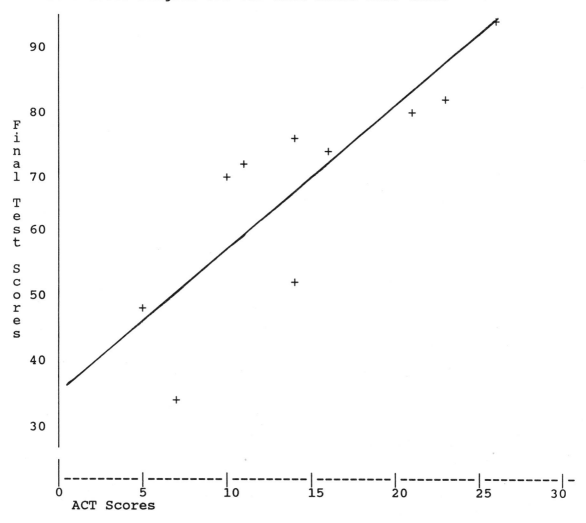

2. Correlation coefficient, r = .827

3. Covariance, COV(x,y) = COV(ACT,Final) = 105.73

4. Least Squares line: $y = b(0) + b(1)x$

   (i) $\bar{x} = 14.7$, $\bar{y} = 69.2$

   (ii) SS(x) = 428.1, SS(xy) = 951.8. So $b(1) = \dfrac{951.8}{428.1} = 2.22$

   and $b(0) = 69.2 - (2.22)(14.7) = 36.524.$

   Thus, the line: $y = 36.524 + 2.22x$

5. SSE = SSY $- \dfrac{SSXY^2}{SSX}$, SSY = 3091.6, so SSE = $3091.6 - \dfrac{951.8^2}{428.1}$

   $= 3091.6 - 2116.15 = 975.45$

6. Error Variance, $s^2 = \dfrac{SSE}{8} = \dfrac{975.45}{8} = 121.93$, and $s = 11.04$

7. Test hypotheses: H(o): BETA(1) = 0

   H(a): BETA(1) =/ 0

   Test statistic: $t = \dfrac{b(1) - BETA(1)}{s/SQRT[SSX]} = \dfrac{2.22 - 0}{11.04/SQRT[428.1]}$

   $= 4.16$

   Test against t(ALPHA/2,df) = t(.05,8) = 1.86.

   Since our computed t* > t(.05,8), we fail to support the null hypothesis; BETA(1) =/ 0.

8. A 90% CI for the slope, BETA(1):

   $b(1) - t(.05,8)s[b(1)] < BETA(1) < b(1) + t(.05,8)s[b(1)]$

   $2.22 - (1.86)(.5336) < BETA(1) < 2.22 + (1.86)(.5336)$

   $1.22754 < BETA(1) < 3.21245$

9. The Strength of the Model:

   $$t* = \dfrac{.827}{SQRT\left[\dfrac{1 - .827^2}{6}\right]} = \dfrac{.827}{.2295} = 3.6032$$

and t(.1,8) = 1.397, so that our computed t* > t.

10. The Coefficient of Determination, r^2 = .827^2 = .684, and

$$\text{directly, } r^2 = 1 - \frac{SSE}{SSY} = 1 - \frac{975.45}{3091.60} = .684$$

11. A 90% CI for MU[y|x = 15]: from the Least Squares line,

y(15) = 36.524 + 2.22(15) = 69.824, and the interval,

$$69.824 - t(.05,8)(11.04)\text{SQRT}[\frac{1}{10} + \frac{(15 - 14.7)^2}{428.1}] < \text{MU}[y|x = 15]$$

$$< 69.824 + t(.05,8)(11.04)\text{SQRT}[\frac{1}{10} + \frac{(15 - 14.7)^2}{428.1}]$$

69.824 - 6.52 < MU[y|x = 15] < 69.824 + 6.52

63.3 < MU[y|x = 15] < 76.345

12. Y for x = 15 with 90% Confidence: we need

$$\text{SQRT}[1 + \frac{1}{10} + \frac{(15 - 14.7)^2}{428.1}] = 1.0489$$

69.824 - (1.86)(11.04)(1.0489) < y < 69.824 + (1.86)(22.04)(1.0489

69.824 - 21.539 < y < 69.824 + 21.539

48.285 < y < 91.363

Chapter 15

1. The Regression Equation is

   C1(Final Test) = 60.5 + 1.22C2(ACT) - 0.16C3(AST)

2. Hypotheses: H(o): BETA(i) = 0 for all i

                  H(a): BETA(i) =/ 0 for at least one i

   Test statistic: F(.1,1,8) = 3.46

   Test: F = $\dfrac{MSR}{MSE}$ = $\dfrac{201.43}{79.08}$ = 2.547

   Our computed F < F(.1,1,8), implying that at least one of
      our coefficients is not pulling its weight. Any guesses?
      [Note the negative coefficient on C3, the coefficient
      for the Arithmetic Skills Test.]

3. Our test statistic, t(.1,8) = 1.397

   The CI for the ACT Scores:

      1.22 - (1.397)(.5444) < BETA(ACT) < 1.22 + (1.397)(.5444)

            1.22 - .7605 < BETA(ACT) < 1.22 + .7605

                  .4595 < BETA(ACT) < 1.9805

   The CI for the AST Scores:

      -0.164 - (1.397)(1.11) < BETA(AST) < -0.164 + (1.397)(1.11)

            -0.164 - 1.5507 < BETA(AST) < -0.164 + 1.5507

                  -1.7147 < BETA(AST) < 1.3867

   There seems to be significant doubt that the AST scores con-
      tribute to the predictive ability of this model--at least
      for this small sample.

4. Our test statistic, $t(.05,8) = 1.86$

   The CI for the ACT Scores:

   $$1.22 - (1.86)(.5444) < BETA(ACT) < 1.22 + (1.86)(.5444)$$

   $$.2074 < BETA(ACT) < 2.2326$$

   The CI for the AST Scores:

   $$-0.164 - (1.86)(.5444) < BETA(AST) < -0.164 + (1.86)(.5444)$$

   $$-2.2286 < BETA(AST) < 2.2326$$

   Note, once again, that increased confidence necessitates a wider interval. The ACT scores seem to be holding; the AST scores dig themselves deeper into the zero hole.

5. Coefficient of determination, $R^2 = 1 - \dfrac{SSE}{SST} = 1 - \dfrac{553.54}{956.40}$

   $$= 1 - .5788 = .4212$$

   and the test, $F = \dfrac{.4212}{\dfrac{1 - .4212}{8}} = 5.8223$

   while the test statistic, $F(.1,1,8) = 3.46$, so that $F* > F$ so we're still in business. But the analysis of the individual factors lets us know we might do better--if this sample reflects the population.

   The information from the MINITAB package is as follows, and explains some of the figures used above:

   The Regression Equation is:

   $$C1 = 60.5 + 1.22C2 - 0.16C3$$

Predictor	Coef	Stdev	t-Ratio
Constant	60.47	27.22	2.22
C2	1.22	0.5444	2.24
C3	- 0.164	1.110	-0.15

   $s = 8.893$ $R^2 = 42.1\%$ $R^2(adj) = 25.6\%$

Analysis of Variance

Source	df	SS	MS
Regression	2	402.86	201.43
Error	7	553.54	79.08
Total	9	956.40	

6. The MINITAB print-out for the regression of the ACT, AST, and Final Test scores on letter grade appears as follows:

The Regression Equation is

$$C1 = -4.03 + .0868C2 + .0002C3 - .0134C4$$

Predictor	Coef	Stdev	t-Ratio
Constant	-4.035	1.057	-3.82
C2	0.08678	0.01124	7.72
C3	0.00018	0.02122	0.01
C4	-0.01338	0.03307	-0.40

$s = 0.2645$ $R^2 = 94.5\%$ $R^2(adj) = 91.7\%$

Analysis of Variance

Source	df	SS	MS
Regression	3	7.1801	2.3934
Error	6	0.4199	0.0700
Total	9	7.6000	

Correlation

	C1	C2	C3
C2	0.971		
C3	0.624	0.648	
C4	0.036	0.077	0.183

Have fun!